THE YALU FLOWS

THE YALU FLOWS

A KOREAN CHILDHOOD

MIROK LI

TRANSLATED BY H. A. HAMMELMANN

WOOD ENGRAVINGS BY JOHN DE POL

THE MICHIGAN STATE UNIVERSITY PRESS

EAST LANSING

First Published in the United States
1956

Library of Congress Catalog Card No. 56-12105

Manufactured in the United States of America

CONTENTS

THE YALU FLOWS

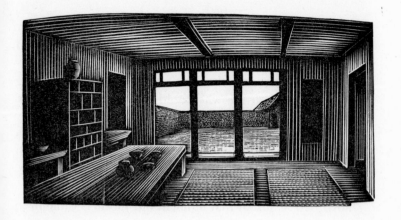

I. *Suam*

SUAM was the name of the cousin with whom I grew up. The first of our joint experiences I can recall was not a happy one. I forget exactly how old we were then; I may have been five and he five-and-a-half. I can still see us sitting one evening with my father, who kept pointing with a little stick at a difficult character in a Chinese primer. Suam was to explain it. He had learnt the signs in the morning, but now on being examined he seemed unable to remember anything. There he sat, neither moving nor uttering a word. My father, who was an ambitious man, had determined to start Suam's Chinese lessons as early as possible because the language was so difficult.

"This character means 'vegetable'. What is it called in Chinese?" he asked impatiently.

"*Tsai*," my cousin replied at once.

"Right," said my father, "and what about the next?"

1

This character seemed more difficult than the first. Suam remained silent, stealing forlorn glances first into one corner of the room and then into the other, and looking desperately even at me who could not possibly help him, because I had not yet begun to read at all.

"What a fool you are!" my father scolded him, and suddenly Suam's narrow eyes began to fill with tears, which rolled down his cheeks until they dropped on the enigmatic character itself. This made me very sad.

Fortunately, just at that moment our mothers came in to fetch us.

"Don't drive the children," my mother said to Father; "they'll learn it anyhow once they go to school."

Gratefully we slipped out of the room.

Suam was my comrade. We played together, had our meals together in the morning and in the evening, and went together everywhere. There were many other children in our house: I had three sisters, and Suam (whose father was dead) had two, so that there were altogether seven of us. Then there was Kuori, chambermaid, laundress, and nursemaid rolled into one; she, too, was counted among the children. But all of them were older than the two of us and all of them were girls, no good for anything. So we two were inseparable. We even wore, if I remember rightly, the same pink blouses with a dark brown belt, the same grey trousers, and the same shoes of black leather. Though Suam was only half a year older than I, there was no danger of anyone taking us for twins. Suam was a strongly built but fat little boy, with round, smooth cheeks. He had strikingly narrow slit eyes, a small, almost lipless mouth, and a graceful nose. I, by contrast, was thin and tall, had large eyes, and a big nose. For all that, we made an inseparable couple and usually laughed and cried at the same time.

The sun shone beautifully in the Rear Court where we played all day. In this quiet, wide court we were left altogether to ourselves, for hardly anyone came there in daytime. When it was hot we would take our clothes off and run about naked. We were surrounded by a high wall; none of the neighbors could see us, and of our sisters or the maid Kuori, who came over occasionally to pick vegetables, we were not shy.

Suam dug a long, straight ditch and covered it with flat stones which I got together. One end of the ditch he made into a stoke-hole, at the other he built a chimney. When that was done we burnt dry sticks in the hole and watched the smoke drifting slowly away through the chimney. We filled in all the slits between the stones with earth until there was no other escape for the smoke. It was a lovely game. Certainly Suam was not a fool, whatever my father had said. He was a good and clever boy.

Another time he showed me how to catch dragon-flies— a thing every boy in our country had to know. You tied together the ends of a thin willow branch and fastened this hoop to a long handle. Thus equipped, you went to search for cobwebs and covered the ring with them as tightly as possible. As soon as we saw a fine dragon-fly, we would chase it, swinging our net about wildly. Suam often made a good catch; he would remove the dragon-fly from the net with great care, holding her by the waist with thumb

3

and index-finger and bending her body forward, until the insect actually bit its own tail. When he caught a cock-chafer, he sometimes laid it on its back upon a broad, smooth stone, where it danced about for a long time, fluttering it wings. We thought that lovely.

When we got tired of running about we sat down on a straw palliasse to sun ourselves. The outer yard was not only our playground. There were also a vegetable plot, a shallow well without water, and a large barn. Balsamine bloomed on the wall, and in the kitchen garden we had cucumbers, pumpkins, and melons with their white and yellow blossoms. Here, too, stood a big pomegranate tree with countless flaming red fruit. We never picked them, for they tasted so bitter.

Our house had several courtyards. The main building, consisting of six rooms, a kitchen, and a covered veranda, was laid out in a circle around a large open space: the Inner Court, where the women lived. Here were a small duckhouse, a dovecot, and a few plants in flower-pots. In front of the house lay two more courtyards, separated only by a low wall with a door. The one on the right-hand side, through which one reached my father's room, was called the well-yard, because of a deep well there; on the lefthand side was the Outer Court, with a high gate and a number of guest-rooms. We were allowed only in this court-yard.

One fine afternoon Suam interrupted our game and led me to the Inner Court and from there into what was called the maid's closet, a room we very rarely entered. I followed my cousin eagerly, because his schemes were always wonderful and exciting. For a while he stood in front of a tall

4

cupboard looking up wistfully at a shining brown pot. I
had seen the pot before, but did not know what might be
in it. Suam got some cushions, placed them one upon the
other, and tried to climb the cupboard. I helped him from
below as best I could. He tumbled down several times,
because Korean cushions are long and round, not flat, but
he did not give in until at last he reached the top. There
he remained for a long time, making odd little sounds as
if he were sucking or eating something. I asked him what
he had found. He made no answer and just went on. Finally
he announced that he would bring down some honey for
me. He put his right hand deep into the pot and then tried
to climb down, holding fast with his left. In the end, alas,
he toppled over, for the cushions rolled away; trying to
steady himself, he reached out with his honeyed hand, and
left smudges everywhere, so that little remained of the
beautiful yellow syrup. Even so, I licked his hand clean,
and then we made off, quite contented and without suspecting in the least what was before us.

In the evening we had to pay the penalty of our sins. We
were already in our beds, Suam in his mother's bedroom
and I in mine. Suddenly someone called us. Hoping for a
sweet melon or a pear, we entered my mother's big room
full of expectancy. Our reception was by no means cordial.
Kuori, the chambermaid, was examining one cushion after
another, while my mother looked decidedly stern. With a
glance of dismay, Suam conveyed to me that the cushions
had given us away. My aunt asked whether we had climbed
the cupboard. Suam said nothing, squinting grimly at his
mother, who had taken up a bamboo stick. She did not,

fortunately, use it to punish, and only slapped our cheeks with her hand, right and left. It hurt me very much, and I started to howl, but from Suam there was not a sound. He seemed to appreciate the justice of the proceedings. He neither cried nor protested, but gently drew me out of the room.

II. *The Poison*

EVERY morning Suam had to learn four new characters.
I sat beside him in my father's room and waited until
he was dismissed. Suam was very slow at learning. It took
him a long time before he was able to repeat the four characters, first separately, then all together, and to explain
their meaning.

Soon lessons began for me, too. One morning my father
placed a new book before me and said: "You have looked
on long enough; now it is your turn."

My book was just like Suam's, bound with blue string
into a yellow cover. I opened it, and my father taught me
the first four characters. I felt very solemn and sat in deep
awe; but Suam was delighted, because from now on we
would learn together and he would no longer have to
struggle alone.

Much better than reading we enjoyed our writing lessons, which began a little later. We each had our own
writing-box and a few sheets of paper; the first job, however, was to grind the Chinese ink. You poured a thimble-
ful of water into the hollow of the black grindstone and
rubbed the ink-stick to and fro until the water became

7

thick and oily. The intoxicating smell of it! After that we got down to it, painting with our coarse brushes, line after line, according to a pattern set before us. Much patience was needed. To start off with, we wrote only one character, "heaven," and practiced that well over a hundred times. We clutched the paint-brush with the whole hand, the way a charwoman handles a broom, and besmeared the beautiful paper from top to bottom. Soon our fingers were coal-black. We wiped them carelessly on our trousers and went on writing. Suam, more impetuous in everything than I was, wrote rapidly, and within a short while his light grey trousers were covered with a criss-cross of black smudges. Even our pink sleeves became blacker and blacker. After the first of our writing lessons all the women in the house were horrified, but there was no punishment. My father defended us and said with good humor: "These are marks of honor for young writing-masters."

Our hands fared worst, because the ink settled in the countless tiny grooves of the palms and could not be removed. We became known as "the two ink-boys," and Kuori, whose task it was to wash me in the morning, gloated over it.

"What I should like to know is this," she used to say, smacking her lips. "Which is blacker—your hands or a crow's foot?"

After we had mastered the character for "heaven," we wrote, or rather painted, the sign for "earth," then for "blue" and "yellow" in the order prescribed by our primer. All writing had to be done on the veranda of the Inner Court, for in the rooms we would have dirtied the clean mats. We did not care. Soon we had learnt to write "sun," "moon," "stars," and "planets."

When our lessons were over we had to leave my father's room at once and were not to enter again unbidden. In no circumstances were we allowed to disturb my father or the guests who often came to visit him. It was difficult to obey this rule because it was just in his room that there were so many beautiful things which we longed to see.

One afternoon, however, the room was empty. My parents and Suam's mother had gone out. That was our chance to examine everything at leisure. We had a good look at the embroidered cushions and bolsters, inspected the writing-desk, peeped into the tobacco jars made of wood or pottery, and finally opened the sliding door of the corner cabinet, where we made the most exciting finds: picture scrolls, a hat-box, and a hollow games-board which you could beat like a drum. Next to the cabinet stood a large, mysterious chest of dark wood with seemingly countless drawers, all of them, alas, locked fast. We dragged, pulled, and pushed as hard as we knew how; but all our efforts were of no avail—the chest just would not yield its secrets. At last Suam discovered a little key, and now we were able to unlock one closet after the other and finger the magical objects which lay hidden there. That was where our luck turned.

Without the slightest suspicion that anything here might be unwholesome, we began to taste of the contents of each drawer. There were leathery white bulbs, thin twigs, little brown capsules, and all sorts of other things. I stuck to the little twigs because they had a faint sugary taste, but Suam was much more thorough and ate many black pills and whitish tablets. After a while he became curiously quiet and sat down in silence.

"Miak," he called out softly, as he always did when he had something special to tell me. He couldn't say an R nor a proper open O. "Miak, fetch me some water!"

I brought him a bowl full, and he emptied it in one gulp. Then he sat still for a while, rather dazed.

"Miak, look at my throat!" he said plaintively, opening his mouth wide. His throat was red and swollen. When I told him, tears came into his eyes. "Die," he announced sadly.

We left everything and ran into the Inner Court. My sisters sent Kuori to fetch the parents. Suam's throat seemed to swell and swell. He could hardly breathe; he suffered terribly. My poor Suam! Never had I seen him so unhappy. Breathing heavily, he lay on the ground without taking his eyes off me, as if he really meant to say good-bye for ever.

At last my father came. He brought with him the doctor, who questioned me closely about what he had eaten and proceeded to prepare a cup of black broth.

That black broth did miracles. Suam was well again next morning, only a little more subdued than usual. He willingly went on drinking the bitter medicine. The doctor seemed to have discovered all sorts of other things which were wrong with him; from now on my friend had to be examined often and to take medicine all the time. He did it without a murmur, knowing that only the black drink had saved his life.

The evil day came when Suam was to receive real pun-

ishment for his greediness. Nobody wished to punish him
as long as he was so ill; for my part, no amount of scolding
and slapping could make any impression on me, anyhow.
I was too pleased that Suam had not died. But now something terrible was in store for him.

One hot afternoon he was taken to see the doctor in
Father's room. The doctor explained to him that he would
light on his back two little heaps of medicinal herbs, so
that the heat could enter into his skin and heal him. When
he had been shown everything, Suam thought it over for a
second or two, and then bent down before the doctor.

"You won't leave me, will you?" he implored me.

"No, I won't go away," I assured him.

The two mothers held his hands, to make sure that he
would keep still. The doctor formed two small pyramids
of a greyish-green substance on his back and lit them at
the top.

"It's smoking," I told Suam.

"Does it hurt already?" the doctor asked.

"No," said Suam bravely. After a moment or two he
added: "Oh, it's getting hot!"

"Just a little longer," the doctor replied. "The strength
of the herbs must enter into the skin." He described a
circle round the burning mound with his finger.

"Oh, oh, it burns!" Suam yelled. "Miak, take that stuff
off my back!"

"A little longer still," the mothers cried, holding me
back.

"Do take the stuff away," Suam howled desperately once
again. "It burns my skin."

"I can't, Suam!"

"Quick, take it away, Miak, away, quick! Miak, Miak! Oh, Miak!"

This heart-rending scene ended with a terrible outburst of invective.

"Oh, you wretch!" Suam screamed; "you doctor, you dog!"

．　　．　　．　　．　　．

During all this time we went on learning from our Chinese primer. It was called *A Thousand Characters,* and that title was written on the cover. There were exactly one thousand characters in it, always four in a row. Beneath the proper title was another, "White-Hair-Script." When at last we got to the end of the whole book, my father explained to us this expression.

The author of the book, so we learned, had been a criminal condemned to death, while still a young man, by the Emperor of China. But he was also a great poet, and for that reason all the citizens begged the Emperor to spare his life. So the Emperor set him a very difficult task; if he could solve it, his life would be spared. The task was this: that in a single night he was to compose a true poem out of a thousand characters arbitrarily chosen by the Emperor himself. The condemned man succeeded in his task, but when he presented himself with his poem the next morning, nobody could recognize him. In that one single night, while he had struggled for his life, he had become an old man. The poem, however, was most beautiful; the Emperor recognized in him a great poet and gave him his life.

We sat at my father's feet and listened to the story

breathlessly. True, we didn't really know what a crime was, nor what sort of crime the poet had committed; but to think that in fighting for his life his hair had turned white made us profoundly sad.

.   .   .   .   .

A big change came into our life when my father hired a teacher for us and opened a sort of domestic school in the outer courtyard, to which the children of friends were invited. From now on both of us were to go every morning to the strange teacher, writing and reading the whole day long under his supervision. We didn't care for this new life at all, because we had to sit still and learn until the evening. The only thing we enjoyed were the breaks, when we could play with the other children, who taught us many new games.

The most popular game among boys was called *zbegi*— a kind of shuttlecock. We made our own balls out of coins (which had slits in the center) and a bit of silken paper. You kicked the ball into the air with one foot, caught it again with the other before it touched the ground, and kicked it up again. Whoever could do this most often without dropping the ball was the winner. Usually we played just for the honor of winning, but among other children the winner was sometimes allowed to chide and rail at the loser, or even to hit him with two fingers on the arm near the wrist. Suam played *zbegi* passionately, but he often started to quarrel when he got excited, and the game would end in kicks and blows.

III. *First Punishment*

Suam sat in the chamber behind the big visitors' room. He was working diligently, splitting a long bamboo stick into fine slivers and shaving the splinters with a sharp knife until they were smooth. He cut a round hole into a large sheet of paper given to him for his writing exercises, and then painted beneath it an ink butterfly. He made a frame of slivers, glued the paper to it, and let the whole thing dry. The result was a paper kite. Often we had seen other children flying such kites on the town walls in front of our house, and longed for one of our own. Alas! this was a wish which our parents failed to grant us. Having thoroughly inspected a kite, Suam was making one of his own. I was full of admiration for my cousin's skill and helped him glue and dry the paper, in the hope that soon our own kite might soar into the sky.

The next day, in secret, we made our first attempt in the backyard, but the kite would not rise; again and again it fell clumsily to the ground. Countless times I ran, throwing it up into the wind, while Suam with the line dashed full speed in the opposite direction. The kite would not move. Suam was disappointed, but he set to work anew with still thinner slivers and even finer paper. He was not in luck. One kite followed after another. He had plenty of paper, for each day he received three new sheets for his writing, and of these he took one for his kites. Moreover, whole piles of the most beautiful paper lay arranged in rows in the chamber, and that, too, he used occasionally. Since nobody came there in the evening, he was able to work quite undisturbed. I returned tired and a little discouraged to my room.

.   .   .   .   .

Lying in bed I used to love looking at the pictures on the wall-screen. It had no fewer than eight panels. There were mountains on it, rocks and flowers, rivers and bridges, and a seashore with wild geese moving across the horizon, and in the candle-light the whole had a wonderful glow. The picture I loved best was that of a shepherd boy riding on a cow and playing his flute. He was just passing a tall weeping willow on the way back to his hut, which was barely visible in the distance among the hills. The sunny road pleased me and the slowly moving cow; the sound of the flute seemed to reach me with its infinite peace.

As I lay there alone I was often joined by my third and youngest sister, who was only two years older than myself. Setye was a strange girl. She did not care to play with the other sisters and cousins when they got together at night in the back court for their various girls' games. Instead she came to me and told me fairy-tales. She knew countless sagas and tales of the stars, of sun and moon, of the swallows, the hares and the tigers, of poor peasants and wood-cutters.

One of her stories was of a simple wood-cutter who went into the mountains to fetch fagots. Suddenly a hazel-nut rolled down the slope. "That is for my mother!" he said and as he picked it up, others came tumbling down until his pockets were full. When he reached home all the nuts had turned into pure gold.

Another fairy-tale told of a poor fisherman who was fishing in a big stream. The whole day long he was out of luck, and he was worried that he might not be able to bring home anything at all. At last in the evening he caught a carp whose scales shone like silver. As he was putting the fish into his basket, he noticed that the carp was crying bitterly. This made the fisherman very sad, so he threw it back into the water. Next morning he was sent for by the King of the Southern Seas and received a present of a charmed wishing-barrel, because the carp whom he had spared was the King's only son, the Prince. The wishing-barrel brought forth every good thing the fisherman could ever wish for.

Like my other sisters, Setye did not go to our school, which was only for boys. Daughters were to be taught the female accomplishments by their mothers and the older women. Setye was still too young. She did not yet know how to sew or embroider, nor how to cook, and spent her days prattling and playing. Sometimes I saw her sitting in the garden twisting squeezed balsam leaves round her little finger. This was to make her finger-nail red, which she considered beautiful. At other times I found her lying in a corner engrossed in reading a fat book. She loved reading stories and romances.

The books she read were written not in the difficult Chinese, but in the easy Korean script which consists of some twenty letters. As Setye explained to me by and by, the individual characters were not called, say, "heaven" or "earth," "sun" or "moon," but A or O, E or K or N. Setye had learned them very early from her foster-mother, and since then she was able to read all tales and romances, which were printed in these characters, so that there should be something to read even for the women who did not usually go to school at all.

Setye enjoyed teaching me. From her I learned counting, the names of the feast days and anniversaries, and many other important things. When she was not telling me fairy-stories, but lying silently beside me, arms under her head, I knew that she was just about to examine me.

"What are the four directions?" she began.

"East, west, south, and north," I replied.

"And what are the colors called?"

"Blue, yellow, red, white, and black."

"And how do the seasons succeed upon each other?"

"Spring, summer, autumn, and winter."

"Which are the beauties that the spring brings?" she continued. She had taught me many proverbs about the beauty of the seasons, and these I was expected to recite.

"On the mountains the flowers are blossoming, and the cuckoo calls from all the valleys."

"Yes, that is so. And what makes the beauty of the summer?"

"A fine rain sprays the fields, and the green leaves of the willows hide the walls."

"And what is beautiful in the autumn?"

"A cool wind sweeps across the fields, dead leaves fall from the trees, and the moon shines into the deserted courtyard."

"That is good. And what does the winter bring?"

"Hills and mountains cover themselves in white, and you will meet no strange wanderer on the path."

"You are very clever!" she praised me.

.   .   .   .   .

One evening I decided to go back to the secret chamber to see how Suam was getting on. He had in the meantime made countless smaller kites; now he wanted to construct a really big one. He told me to paint two large butterflies in black ink below the round hole, while he himself prepared the bamboo sticks. The glue was being warmed and the iron had been placed in the red-hot fire-basin. We were just sticking the bamboo slivers onto the paper, when suddenly the door opened, and there was my father. We were completely taken by surprise and did not know what to do. In the hurry Suam had no chance to hide the kite. My father had already seen it. For a short while he looked with amazement at us, the kite, and the used roll of paper; then he called out angrily:

"Come out of here at once!"

We crept out of the room, and the beautiful kite had to be left behind.

"He only watched me!" Suam spluttered, to save me from punishment.

And that followed next morning. Kite-building alone might not have been so bad; the worst crime was the misuse of the paper which was given to us for our calligraphy lessons and the opening of the precious paper rolls. The teacher was told of our misdeed, and it was he who punished us. We had to pull up our trouser-legs and were beaten on the calves with bamboo sticks. At all times a few such sticks, of the thickness of a finger, were within the teacher's reach, but never before had he made use of them. Now we two were to be the first of the whole peaceful school to serve as a warning example to the rest. All the children were placed round the walls to watch, while we two delinquents had to sit in the center of the room. It was very solemn—painfully solemn! The teacher put his graduate's cap on his head, once again carefully explained our misdeed, took up one of the sticks and tested its toughness. Oh, how awful! He commanded Suam to free his calves. Suam gave the sticks a suspicious glance and remained stiffly seated.

"Won't you come here of your own accord?" the teacher called out.

Suam sighed, stood up before him, and pulled up his trousers. Three strokes came in rapid succession and Suam, my friend, began to cry. Then he declared that I was totally and absolutely innocent, that I had only watched him make the kites. Even so, I too received three strokes, which hurt very much. Yet the pain was not the worst—that I was able to bear. Much more unpleasant was the shame of being beaten in front of all the children who watched us with so much pity.

IV. *At the South Gate*

Almost all the school-children were older than the two of us and therefore further advanced in their lessons. A few already knew the greatest poets of the Tang dynasty and wrote exercises in rhyme, much to the envy of the others. These verses invariably spoke of flowers, rain, moonlight, or cups of wine. Most of the other pupils were studying the great historical work called *Tongam,* which extended to no less than fifteen volumes. It made most fascinating reading. Nations were at war with each other, dynasties were overthrown, and others arose to replace them. The two of us—Suam and I—and the smaller children were still on the modest boy's book which taught the five so-called moral laws and a concise version of Korean history. At last, to our delight, we were through with this primer and received the first volume of the big history.

In the morning, when the teacher entered the classroom, every child had to make a deep and solemn bow. Then followed questions to discover whether we remembered yesterday's lesson. A new task was given to those who passed the test; anything forgotten had to be studied again. When all the children had been examined, each got out his rubbing-stone to prepare Indian ink and practiced calligraphy from a new sample provided by the teacher. After a short interval we read the lessons prepared for the day. Since every child read aloud, and each one from a different book and from a different place, the whole classroom hummed like a beehive.

In the afternoons we had more recesses than in the mornings, and in summer-time we were often sent bathing. Many fine brooks passed through the gorges of our Suyang mountain, and here we ran about, bathed, and played. The very road to such a stream was beautiful. As we left our town behind us we came along a shady path lined on both sides with stone monuments, until we reached a large, deep pond. At once we threw off our clothes and jumped headlong into the clear, cool water. We stayed until the worst heat was over and the air had become less heavy. Then we walked back along the beautiful path. In the trees the cicadas rasped their repetitive refrain.

After supper our mothers allowed us to go for a little while to the South Gate. This we loved. The two-storied tower-house presented a glorious sight in the setting sun. We hurried through the narrow, winding lane between the town wall and our row of houses and climbed the seemingly countless stone steps to the open square in front of the tower building, where the children of the neighborhood were already gathered to play. Some threw old worn coins on the ground and tried to hit them with little flat stones, some played feather-ball, and others hopped back and forth over a given stretch on one leg until they collapsed. They chattered, boasted, quarreled, and fought each other; yet as soon as the opening bars of the music from the Three Gates reached us, all fell silent. The Three Gates were a long distance away, right in the center of the town by the Governor's official residence, but in the calm of the evening the heavenly sound was carried marvelously and clearly to the South Gate and lulled us slowly into the dusk. It was the evening salute offered by the Governor. The day was drawing to a close, night was falling, and all citizens of the town could go to rest free from fear. Peace was over our country!

Yes, the peace of evening had come. Smoke rose from all the houses, and the grey roofs slowly dissolved into the mist of the summer night. Only the highest summits of the mountains still shone brightly into the blue sky. At this time I often felt sad, perhaps because one more day had gone and inexplicable night now enveloped us.

While we sat in self-forgetting, a tall man slowly began to mount the stone steps, entered the tower hall, unlocked the gate of the bell house, and took up a heavy hammer. For a while he stood quite still and listened to the music. When it had died away, he swung the hammer back and struck the giant bell; a roar thundered out deep into the mountains. We stood around the keeper and counted on our fingers the number of his strokes. First we bent in all the right hand, from thumb to little finger, and then we stretched them out again in reverse order. That made ten —quickly we bent in the thumb of the left hand to start counting once more with the right. Every evening there were twenty-eight strokes, because the evening bell was devoted to the earth, which is ruled by the twenty-eight gods of destiny.

Now the gatekeeper was content; he descended the steps, not without admonishing us to go home at once, before the little evening goblins would throw stones at us. The children obeyed him; they squatted on the broad stone balustrade and began to slide down. We did the same; much sliding had made the stone quite smooth and clean, so the bottoms of our trousers could not become any dirtier than they were already.

We walked up to the archway to make sure that the South Gate was firmly closed and that the pie-man had set up his stall in the usual place. His delicious slices, round, square and oblong, were laid out on a broad board, arranged according to size and ingredients. Near them were a small lamp and a pair of scissors with which to cut the slices. From time to time the pie-man would praise with melancholy chants the various spices which he had mixed into his wares, beating the rhythm with his small scissors.

Satisfied and at peace, we made our way home through the darkening lane. We were not afraid of the goblins. A weak light from some of the houses already fell across our way, and within we still felt warmed by the sweet melody of the evening music.

I went for a short while into our back court-yard to watch the girls at their games, but Suam sometimes stole away, not to return until late. The boys of our quarter of the town assembled in some lane or on a square to fight the children of another district, who, being inhabitants of a strange quarter, were considered enemies. Mostly they fought only with their fists, but occasionally sticks or even little stones served as weapons. The cooler the evenings became and the brighter the moon, the more frequent these fights. On such occasions Suam's jacket often looked grim.

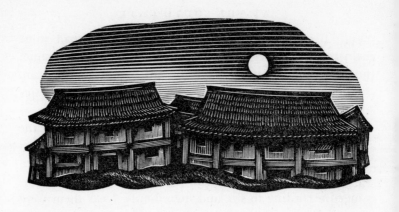

V. *Seven Stars*

WITH his relatives my father did not seem to have much luck. His brother died young and left him his widow and three children to look after. Then the husband of his sister died, and she came to join us at the end of her mourning years with her only son. He was about ten years of age and the eldest of us three, a very good-looking boy, with his red cheeks, slender and gracefully built, like most boys at that age. His beauty was marred by one flaw only: his lips were extraordinarily thick and hard. We were told that they had become like that after a serious illness. His eyes were bright and lively and his ears marvelously rounded. The color of his face was so delicate and that of his cheeks so rosy that he might have been taken for a girl had he not worn boy's clothes. What surprised me even more were his inordinately clean hands. When I looked at my own, I realized the big difference between him and me.

One evening we were playing our usual game of feather-ball in the Fountain Court when he suddenly appeared. Walking up, he asked which was Suam and which Mirok. We knew immediately who stood before us. It was Seven Stars, the new cousin who was to live with us from now on. I liked him at once because he was so beautiful. Immediately I asked him to join us. Suam did not seem to care for this; he leant against the fountain and refused to continue the interrupted game. "It is too cold to play here," he said, and viewed with disdain the new-comer who looked so frail.

After we had continued our game of *zbegi* for a while, Seven Stars took from his pocket a short bamboo flute and began to play on it. Through his thick lips he blew first a smart, lively tune, and then a slow, melancholy one, which brought back pleasant memories. I felt a marvelous lightness in my limbs, and soon I saw that Suam's body was moving with the rhythm. I, too, began to dance, and Seven Star's music became more and more passionate. He blew and blew; intoxicated by our dance, we failed to notice that my father and an old gentleman, the grandfather of Seven Stars, had appeared on the veranda outside my father's room and were smilingly watching us.

My father had never seen me dance. I could not remember him in my mother's room any of the evenings when we performed there under the direction of my grandmother. My two older sisters would beat the rhythm on a small drum and sing childish melodies, while we moved our arms and legs as best we knew. But never had our sisters sung so beautiful and moving a song as this one.

It was a tune from the so-called Valley Dance, a popular pantomime which was performed in our town once a year. One fine spring morning, several seasons ago, Kuori had taken Suam and me to the town to watch this spectacle. There we joined the throng which was following about thirty masked dancers accompanied by a band through the whole town to the open-air stage outside the North Gate. All around the theatre the spectators sat packed on the town walls, on the gatehouse, and on the slopes under the tall shady trees.

The first person to appear on the stage was an old priest who had left his monastery to come to town. Here he fell in love with a beautiful woman, and this filled him with such happiness that he felt compelled to dance. He was joined eventually by a gay fool with a cluster of bells which jingled at every movement he made. In the end the fool confused the priest's wooing so much that he was able to elope with the beauty himself. Nothing remained for the poor old man but to return again to his mountain and his monastery. His leave-taking—a dance full of rhythm but very sad—formed the end of the performance which had lasted the whole day.

This final dance began as the sun was setting and continued well into the dusk. It moved me deeply. To see the old man swinging his all-too-long sleeves back and forth to the nostalgic melody, to watch him set his tired feet slowly and deliberately, to see his back, now erect, now bent, as he moved in a sad circle—all this so penetrated my heart and mind, that on this occasion I was able to repeat the dance myself. My father openly shared our joy that we three cousins had spent so harmoniously our first evening together.

We had, indeed, a very peaceful autumn and winter. My elder cousin taught us many novel games which delighted us. As soon as school was over we went down to the ice-bound river and played with our spinning-tops until darkness. At home we carved all sorts of toys: tops, bamboo flutes, bamboo sticks, little tobacco boxes, and ashtrays.

. . . . .

At the turn of the year we celebrated the biggest family feast of my homeland. It began around midnight, when sacrifices were offered at the altars of our ancestors. Then we children were called into my mother's big room and regaled with the finest dishes and fruit; we could stay up as long as we pleased. Next morning, dressed in our best, we were sent out to pay New Year visits to all relatives and friends. The cold was severe, the roads were ice-bound and very slippery, a biting wind stung our faces, but, full of excitement and joy, we ran from house to house to give messages which we had learned by heart. Everywhere our hosts received us with words of kindness and offers of sweets and fruit. What a happy feast-day that was, when one heard only friendly and flattering words and was offered nothing but sweets to eat! At home, everybody, from grandmother down to Kuori, was in his best garments, all wore smiles throughout the day, and no one spoke an unpleasant word. Even rough Sunok, who lived with us as bailiff and always called me a good-for-nothing, proved cheerful and gentle that day and remarked that perhaps I might become a proper man one day after all. Everybody joked with us and gave us presents, and as we went to sleep late at

night—for some time now Suam and I had shared a room
—my mind became blissfully aware that there were still a
whole fifteen days without lessons ahead. "How beautiful
the world is!" I said to myself. But Suam was already
snoring.

After the children, it was the turn of the adults to pay
their calls. Numberless visitors—girls and women, young
and old men—came to our house, which was filled with
gaiety and laughter. In this way feast day followed feast
day in unending succession.

While I lost count of time in this festive mood, Suam
would quietly disappear in the evenings and return home
very late. Among the boys New Year battles had begun,
and he could not resist the temptation of taking part. His
beautiful clothes bore traces of kicks and nose-bleeding
which he attempted with great care to remove. One evening he returned in a terrible state. The two sleeves were
half torn off and his head was bruised and swollen in many
places. He told me that, when they had taken him prisoner,
three hostile boys had beaten him until he was freed by a
comrade. This experience seems to have cooled somewhat
his ardor for battle; during the next few evenings he
remained quietly at home, although the fighting became
more violent than ever and the decision of the whole war
was but a few days off.

Instead we began another battle at home among the
three of us. This battle was brought about by none other
than my father himself. One evening when there were no
visitors in the house he called us to his room and showed
us a remarkable game. All the ranks and titles of officials,

from the highest to the lowest in the land, were drawn up
on a stiff roll of paper. We were to begin our career at the
bottom of the ladder, and he was the winner who first
achieved the rank of senator. Father took up a book and
opened it at random. The first word of the page was chosen
as the rhyme word, and each one of us was to recite a classical poem which ended on this word. Whoever succeeded
was allowed to begin his career. Seven Star's first word was
"ruler." For a long while he remained silent, for he knew
no poem with such an ending. Then it was Suam's turn;
his word was "spring"—so common a word in verse that
we envied his good luck. After a little stuttering he said:
"Along the lanes nested the spring." "Good!" said my
father and appointed him to the rank of Scribe of Literature. That was a great performance of Suam's, but unfortunately it remained his first and last. He received no further promotion because he did not receive another easy
rhyme word. He had read only one volume of poems, and
even these he no longer knew by heart. Seven Stars and I
did not make a great deal more progress: his promotions
stopped after the third and mine after the fourth. There
was no winner.

A few days later we resumed the game, but this time not
as a contest of poets but as a struggle among dice-throwers.
It was Seven Stars who had discovered that this made the
game much simpler. We all became officials at once and
received continuous promotion; the whole game was decided in half an hour. Each victory was worth one copper
coin. My father did not in truth like this way of playing,
but he helped us none the less, and gave fascinating expla-

nations about the rank and power of each individual official and how one reached such a position in real life.

Suam was very keen on the post of Governor of our
province ever since we had seen his solemn entry into the
town the year before. This powerful man had been received by his staff of officials some three miles outside the
boundaries. There he had partaken of his first meal within
his future domain before riding into the town. We, accompanied by Kuori, stood among the crowd who had taken
up their position in front of the houses. From far off we
heard the glorious music, and then, through the South
Gate, we had our first sight of the cavalcade. Ahead rode
five double rows of musicians on chestnut horses, followed
by about forty mounted maidens in gay silk costumes and
ten pairs of high dignitaries in their solemn black attire.
They were Deputy Governnors of our province, which was
still divided into its twenty-three sub-provinces. After that
the Governor himself rode past with two beautiful young
men, his personal servants. His steed was as white as his
hair. The hat he wore was a kind of top hat crowned with
snow-white feathers and fastened under the chin with
strings of amber. Behind the Governor followed countless
clerks and officials. On little Suam the great man had made
an immense impression.

For myself, I was more taken by the so-called *Osha*. This
was the man who travelled all over the country to straighten
out injustices and see to it that all the King's subjects did
their duty. By a mere report to the king he could dismiss
the mightiest official or promote the humblest. Of course
he walked across the country unrecognized, usually dis-

guised as a beggar, so that nobody knew when he was near. The stories we had already been told about this *Osha* were innumerable. He had brought rice and money to many poor families and given freedom to innocent prisoners. I wished to become such an *Osha* who looked like a beggar, had a train of many hundred unrecognized servants, and was yet a man of power without equal. When I held this position in our game and threw a six, all other officials were exiled until they themselves succeeded in getting a six. Meanwhile I was able to continue my career alone— in the comfortable post of Senator I awaited the runners-up and had no more rivals to fear.

To suffer banishment of this kind, on the other hand, was gravely resented, especially when it occurred more than once in a game. Suam was often sent into exile, and at this he flew into a terrible rage, particularly, I noticed, when this penalty was inflicted by Seven Stars. In the long run his anger became quite personal, so that almost every evening we went to bed cross. Suam always lost, and soon there was nothing left of the riches he had collected during the New Year days. I lost, too. Seven Stars won everything. Actually, my two cousins had never got on very well. The one was too temperamental, the other too calm, and on top of that Seven Stars was always held out to Suam as a model child. And indeed he was always just too clean! After months his clothes looked like new, while nothing Suam ever wore remained clean for more than three days. Thus the eldest cousin had become a thorn in our flesh. Threatening clouds had long been gathering over our heads, and the smallest spark was sure to release the most violent thunderstorm. This game was the very thing. By the end of our school holidays I had also lost all my money. We were playing for my last copper coin. My father was not at home. Seven Stars had sent me into exile. I came back, was banished again, and came back once more. Suam, whose money had run out long before, was merely watching us. Seven Stars threw up the dice to send me back into exile. Before the dice landed, however, Suam fell upon him violently and caught hold of his long hair. On the ground the two rolled from one corner into the other. I helped Suam a little. Oh, how good it was to see that model boy for once with a bloody nose and a torn jacket.

That was the end of our community.

Judgement came swiftly, but it was not very just. I had thought that Seven Stars ought to receive the worst punishment because he had won everything and thus caused the quarrel. Suam deserved the punishment next in severity, because he had done most of the beating. But in the end the opposite happened. Seven Stars was acquitted and left my father's room unmolested. Suam received from my father three strokes on the calves, which he accepted without crying.

"And now it is your turn!" said our judge.

I, however, refused to bare my legs, for how could I understand why Seven Stars should go scot-free and only Suam and I should be punished?

But Suam poked me in the ribs to tell me to bare my calves. I did so with much hesitation, and already my father began hitting. My opposition availed me little, for he was strong and held me so fast that I could not escape.

After three lashes I turned to tell him that it was high time for the other cousin to have his share. Immediately I received another stroke, and this time it was on the shin, which hurt awfully. I screamed. Suam rushed in and tried in vain to wrench the birch stick from my father; but he, too, received a painful blow on his back quarters and retired whimpering. I got many more strokes—ten at least.

Then my father said: "Now you have had what you deserve!"

But I did not go away.

"Go on," I said stubbornly.

"What!" he called out, and began to beat me again.

Now Suam threw himself once more between us; after a real struggle he snatched the stick out of my father's hand and ran away with it. I was removed from the room by force.

"Be off with your obstinacy and take it where you like, you pig-head!"

VI. *Two Mothers*

IN spring Seven Stars and his mother left us. They moved into a small house in a neighboring lane. Whether Seven Stars' mother wanted a larger household of her own or whether it was our quarrel which put an end to our living all of us together, I do not know. In any case, the separation was very salutary. We did not quarrel any more when we met. Suam and I were even ashamed of having beaten up our elder cousin. True, he was provokingly clean, but that was not his fault.

Shortly after they left, a very strange visitor, an old woman from a distant province, arrived at our house. She spoke of me as her little son. My mother told me to call her Mother. Although she had not given birth to me, it was explained, she had prayed on behalf of my mother for a son and heir, and thus had helped to bring me into the world. She was, in other words, a woman who intercedes and prays for those who desire a child. She was by no means to be confused either with a soothsayer, who goes from home to home with her book of oracles and her painted fan to tell fortunes, nor with a *shaman* woman who conjures up spirits through music and dancing. Her rank was far more exalted, and had nothing to do with

the lesser things of life. She prayed directly to the Master
of Heaven in the name of Buddha and of one of his dis-
ciples. No sooner had my mother heard of this woman
than she set out on the road to beg for her intercession,
for she lived in great anxiety that she might become old
without having borne a son. She found the intercessor,
who came to our home to say this prayer which was to
take her forty-nine days. It was addressed to Buddha's
disciple, the blessed Mirok, whose name I was eventually
given.

One evening, a few days after her arrival, I went into
the forest with my two mothers. There, before a statue of
Saint Mirok, we were to say a prayer of thanks. Far from
the town, deep in a remote valley, stood the little shrine
with the life-size likeness of the saint cut in stone. My
spiritual mother fetched the key from the nearby village,
unlocked the door, and lighted a candle. Darkness was
already upon us; uneasily I stood between my two mothers
gazing upon the statue, which shone brightly in the candle-
light. The saint's expression was calm and peaceful. His
eyes were lowered. His ears were remarkably long, his
arms closely pressed to his body. His hands were tightly
interlocked, while his legs had remained unshaped and
their actual form was only hinted at by the sculptor.

My second mother set fire to a thrice-folded sheet of
paper and, looking into the face of the stone image, began
her prayer. I did not understand all she murmured, for
I was too deeply moved by the sight of the white shining
saint in the dark forest and by the thought that to his
kindly meditation I owed my existence on earth. On our

way home, after the prayer was ended and the shrine had been closed, I felt a great sense of gratitude to the good spiritual intercessor who had made possible my entrance into this world. Without her prayers I should have been born somewhere else and would have had to grow up without Suam, without Kuori, and without my sisters. I tightened my grip on her hand, and she repeated from time to time: "My beloved child."

She gave me many presents. Before going to town she never failed to ask whether there was anything I wanted, and there was not one wish which remained unfulfilled. One day she brought me a large Greek tortoise which was to give me immense delight. I had never seen anything like this animal. The back resembled a beautifully carved ink-box, and I was awestruck when I noticed, clearly engraved on the belly, the Chinese character for "king".

My last four-legged friend had been a small lovely squirrel which became quite tame. Every evening when I came back from the school-yard it had jumped around my face and neck and tumbled about in my sleeves until I gave it a peanut or a chestnut. After I had told my second mother of all this, and also of my regrets that the little squirrel had finally run away, she brought me the tortoise.

Only rarely, and then most cautiously, did I touch the tortoise on the back. Nor was there much else I could do with her. She was so very different from the squirrel. She neither jumped nor screamed, but only moved slowly about the veranda, or might not stir at all for hours on end. She looked most distinguished and regal, and appeared to be deep in thought. My spiritual mother explained that the tortoise was meditating on the fate of man and was able to forecast good and ill fortune. The way to discover the future was to bend forward until one's back was absolutely horizontal, then to place the animal on one's spine and wait until it crawled down. A descent on the right-hand side was taken for a good omen, on the left hand for an ill one. Suam and I bent our backs right to the ground each morning and waited until the tortoise, often after considerable deliberation, made up her mind to climb down. I could not help feeling somewhat uneasy whenever she began to crawl towards the left. Suam advised me to raise my left shoulder very slightly so that it was easier for her to move towards the right. Once the oracle had spoken, we left the tortoise alone; for the rest of the day she lumbered on her solitary phlegmatic round through the two courtyards. She lived on cucumbers and melons, of which we brought her ample supplies. We were told that in the southern land where they grow up these miraculous animals live only on the dew which falls on their lips each morning at sunrise.

. . . . .

It was midsummer again. My second mother had left us. The heat was so intense that there were lessons only in the mornings. In the afternoons we could go to the brooks and bathe as long as we liked. By then we had become good swimmers and dared even to go into deep water. The water of all the mountain streams was crystal clear, so that one could see the pale gleam of rocks and sand many feet below. Sometimes we swam like frogs, dived to the bottom, or floated on our backs at the whim of the current. At others we would stretch out on the rocks, close our eyes, and listen to the lapping waters.

Suam and I invariably brought the tortoise, for she, too, enjoyed a good swim. On the way there and back we wrapped her in a big melon leaf to protect her from the hot sun. Only once did we forget to take her. That was the day on which the tragedy occurred. It seems that she had a great desire for water, and being left alone, had sought it everywhere. When we returned in the evening to feed her, she was nowhere to be found. We searched the whole house; everybody helped. Gradually dusk fell and it bcame dark. The melon-flowers stood out brightly against the night, and bats flapped about close to our heads. But the tortoise was nowhere to be seen. Everyone carried a candle or a wick, and we searched each room in turn, the corn stores, and the ditches in the garden. Finally, Kuori discovered the missing animal in a cooking-pot. She had ceased to move and lay motionless whichever way one put her on the ground. She was dead.

Next day Suam took his spade to the backyard, where he built a little earth mound on which to bury our friend. In those days there were no graves on the flat in Korea; every family owned its own mountain, and on it was one's family graveyard. We, too, therefore wanted to bury the tortoise on a mound. Suam spent the whole afternoon digging until the heap was almost three feet high. I constructed a rough bier of two thick branches and a piece of rope, and on this we carried the animal to her grave. There she lay throughout the whole day. We offered a bowl of water (in the place of wine) as a sacrifice to the mountain spirit and to our dead playmate, so that the soul of the departed would find peace. At sunset we buried the corpse. By the time the tiny grave was closed we were profoundly sad.

Tortoises are said to have a long life, sometimes several thousand years. The death of such a miraculous animal in our house was sure to augur ill for the future.

VII. *My Father*

SOME months later my father fell ill. He had gone on a journey, but returned again within a day or two, and the whole house was set in great commotion. What his illness was I did not know. I only saw that he lay motionless in his room. He kept his eyes closed and did not speak. My mother, my grandmother, and my aunt—Suam's mother—sat around his bed. Many doctors came into the house, but they were unable to do anything for him. Throughout the whole night and the next forenoon he never stirred, yet he was not asleep, for he understood my mother when she asked him to take his medicine. Towards dusk all hope of recovery was abandoned. My mother fainted and had to be carried to her room. The silence of death fell over the whole house. The women were assembled in my father's room, the men on the veranda just outside. No one spoke. Only my aunt attempted again and again to give him the medicine which he was no longer able to swallow.

My mother rested in her room. She had recovered, but would not speak, and only held my hand tightly in hers. When my grandmother came into the room she exclaimed: "This is the end of us all, Mother!" Grandmother did not hear her. She sat down and mumbled to herself. Just then Osini, my second sister, joined us with the news of the arrival of yet another doctor for whom we had already sent in the morning. Suam and I hastened to my father's room.

This new doctor was a man of high reputation and much in demand. He had been in our town for several weeks to visit his patients and was just about to return home. Only the persistence of our messenger brought him to the house. The doctor did not look at my father for long before he spoke to the aunt.

"He is lost," he said. "I would rather not interfere."

"Please try once more!" my aunt whispered, and I saw that she was paler than the patient himself. She held the strange man by the sleeve and prevented him from leaving. "You shall have anything you can ask for."

The doctor sat down again; he examined pulse and heart and then the body of the sick man.

"I will do what I can," he said, "but don't reproach me if the attempt fails."

He drew a leather case out of his pocket and took from it a long needle, with which he pricked first the upper and then the lower lip of the patient. Then he pushed the needle deep into the stomach immediately below the curve

41

of the ribs, left it there for a moment and slowly drew it forth again.

"If the patient is to live, he will give a sign of life before the evening," he said, and walked out of the room.

Evening came; the whole family took hope, for it seemed a promising sign that Father was no worse. He still lay quietly, as he had done in the morning. Outside it was already dark when he moved his hands a little so that they touched. We watched each one of his movements eagerly. Suddenly he opened both eyes and looked around. A sigh of relief went through the room. Then he closed his eyes again and turned to the left so that his face was hidden from us. He fell asleep, breathing like a man in good health.

"He is alive!" said my aunt and burst into irrepressible tears; she was no longer strong enough to rise and had to be helped back to her room.

Meanwhile my mother had heard the good news. She came into Father's room, and could hardly believe that he had taken a turn for the better. She herself looked almost dead, and trembled all over. Gradually she grew calmer and sent us all out of the room with orders for the kitchen and a message to the doctor. Suam and I had to go to bed, and fell asleep at once. When I woke after midnight and ran into the sick room, I found my father sitting up, talking to Mother. I rushed up to them, and he held me on his lap until my mother drew me to herself. I could not keep my eyes off him; again and again I had to reassure myself that he really was alive. At last I settled down beside his bed and fell asleep again, while my parents continued to talk softly of the doctor who had performed this miracle.

Indeed, what a doctor! He was a true miracle-man. Later I heard that he had given new life to many people in our town and all over the country. Once he even returned to life, so it was said, a man who was just being taken to his burial. Alas! the fees he demanded were so exorbitant that the poor could not afford to call him. One day, returning from a visit to a rich patient, he was struck by a stone weighing more than a hundredweight. His crushed body was found just below the town wall. Nobody knew who had done the deed. There were those who said that his heavy sack of gold had turned into stone.

My father recovered very slowly. Throughout autumn and winter he was looked after with the greatest care. He even had to give up the work which hitherto he had been able to do despite his gout. Now he shut his home firmly against the outside world. Social commitments were given up and none but his closest friends came to see us. At first he was very loth to obey the instructions of the doctor and the insistent appeals of the family, but gradually he himself came to realize that he needed rest. He retired more and more into himself. In the end, he even changed the life of the household; the private school was given up and the pupils returned to their homes, never to come back. Once again the outer court lay almost deserted. Only Sunpil, the young clerk, Pang, the old servant, and Sunok, the bailiff, were allowed to live there.

A family council was held. What was to happen to Suam? It was decided that he should continue at school so as to learn Chinese. He was to move with his mother to the country, to a village with a school which gave good classical teaching. My aunt was to look after the management of one of Father's farms which had hitherto been under his personal care. For the two of us, after a whole childhood spent together, this was the first important leave-taking. I walked with Suam all the way to the Dragon's Pond, a bay more than an hour from our town. A boat took him across the sea to the wild craggy shore on the other side. Sitting between his mother and Dulche, his sister, he looked back to us anxiously while the sail was being hoisted and the boat slowly drifted on the restless blue waves.

Once our household had been reduced, our life again took up its old course. My father, however, underwent a great change. He began to introduce Buddhist literature and ceremonies into our house, and from then on he spent several hours in prayer every evening. No rain, no wind, no visitors, no domestic disturbance would hinder him. I could not understand a single word of the prayers because he said them in Sanskrit. I assumed, however, that they were all concerned with his future life.

My mother was pleased, because she herself believed wholeheartedly in the Buddhist teaching. When summer came she suggested that we should visit the temple "Light of God" to say our prayers there. She invited a priest from this monastery to teach her about the various ceremonies and offerings. Eventually the plan had to be postponed until the next summer. I was very sorry about that.

Although the mountains around our little town were dotted with countless monasteries and shrines, I had never seen a temple. Never once had we brought offerings to Buddha, and the big prayer had never been said for us in a temple. The mendicant monks who called at the houses and ran through their prayers outside our gates hardly helped to make the mundane townspeople more religious. Only once a year, on the eighth of April—the day when the divine Buddha resumed his baths after his nineteenth meditation and began to preach—festive Buddhist celebrations took place in our town. High trees, often four times taller than the houses themselves, were set up all along the main street. The trunks were swathed and decorated with multi-colored pieces of cloth, and from the branches countless gay ribbons were spread out to the roofs and to the ground. At night colored paper lanterns hung from the ropes and ribbons, and made you feel as if you were walking through a garden filled with iridescent flowers.

I was very anxious to see a temple, especially the temple "Light of God," which my parents had mentioned so often. One fine morning, on a sudden impulse, I joined two other boys on an excursion to the temple. I had met my old school friends near the West town gate as I was about to return home from my morning walk. I asked them where they were going, and was told quite briefly: "To the 'Light of God'!" The name, when I heard it, went right to my heart, and without hesitation I accepted the invitation to go along with them.

I stepped out bravely and did not worry about anything that was to come. And what a beautiful walk it was! Soon we left our little town behind us, penetrating deeper and deeper into the gorges, until we were hemmed in by mountains on all sides. The sun was beating down upon us, and we sweated heavily. This did not prevent us from walking steadfastly on until at last in the distance we saw a courtyard surrounded by trees. Grey roofs were gleaming through the leaves. They were the roofs of the monastery "Light of God."

It was not until after our arrival that I noticed with alarm the long shadows thrown by the trees; already the sun was low in the west. I begged the others to be on our way home again at once, lest we should be too late. Their answer was that it was too late anyway, and that we should have to spend the night at the monastery. Since my parents did not know where I was, this was the last thing I wished to do. I pressed for our return, but without avail; they wanted first to see the temple. While we were arguing, the sun sank lower and lower, and the young monk who had received us insisted that we could not possibly return during the night along the dangerous paths. I had to give in, and thus it was that I spent my life's first night of sorrow in these mountains.

I hardly saw the glorious halls with their countless statues, did not hear what the monk told us about them, could not eat of the dishes which he brought us. My eyes were fixed upon the mountains which robbed me of the sight of our little town. Nowhere did I discover an open valley, nowhere a glimpse of the familiar sea. Steep summits towered above me, and the evening peal of the temple bell died away forlorn among the mountain crags. Now monks dressed in yellow robes, with prayer-beads

46

fastened round their hands, entered the courtyard to perform their evening rites. Out of the halls of the temple poured light from the thousands of candles on the offertory tables placed all round the walls. Here the monks and descendants of the dead said the big prayer for the souls of the departed.

Broken only by short intervals, this prayer went on throughout the night. Towards dawn the worshippers stepped out into the open and began to circle the courtyard in stately procession; the monks, more than a hundred of them, in their gorgeous vestments, the women in garments of mourning. Each one held in her hands a wooden tablet on which was placed a sheet of paper rolled in the shape of a cylinder, the abode (so I was given to understand) of a departed soul. From the centre of the large circle the sacred log fire threw a mellow glow into the dawn. The muffled bells sounded out their solemn, slow rhythm, while the choir of the monks sang the prayer for the departed and the Namuhamitabul. Now at last was the time for the souls of the dead to be freed from this earth and to enter another existence. Enraptured by the steady drone of the wooden bells and the rhythmical song, we three boys joined the moving circle. Day was slowly breaking, the faces of the men became clearer, faint light fell upon the mountains. The fervor of the prayer reached exaltation and an ardent intensity seized the worshippers. Now in the east a red light rose above the mountains and the first rays of the sun touched us. While the monks continued their chant one woman after another approached the fire and threw the abode of the

47

soul into the flames. The women sobbed and wailed, for this was a last farewell for eternity. We boys also burst into tears. Sombre and mellow the rhythm of the wooden bells rang into the morning and unceasingly the monks carried on the Namuhamitabul.

. . . . .

Much moved by the experience of this night, I took my leave of the mountains and started on my way back.

At home I accepted every reprimand and punishment without a word of protest. This religious experience had strangely shaken me; I felt far more grown up than the day before. My father soon forgave me and asked to be told of everything I had seen. He appeared pleased by it, and from then on even allowed me to pray with him a small part of his evening prayers. After that he told me of the monasteries and temples which lie scattered among the ravines of the Yangtse valley and of the many famous poets who had visited them and praised them in their songs.

Just then in my Chinese lessons I was reading the poets of the Tang dynasty. But rather than read narratives and poems out of books, I preferred to hear my father tell his own stories—sagas and anecdotes of the Tang dynasty. In those days there had been so many unhappy poets, so many beautiful maidens who, tortured by longing for their lovers, sought death in the waters of the river. Nostalgic melodies floated across from the rocks and the groves into deserted valleys, and sad parting songs hovered in the rising evening mist over Tungting lake.

On fine moonlit evenings a seat was prepared for my father under the peach-tree in the fountain court. The

stories he told there were his most poetic; he never tired
of telling them and from time to time even made up his
own poems. All trace of paternal severity was gone. He
joked with me when he succeeded in finding a good rhyme.
Once he even enticed me to drink a few bowls of wine
with him.

This happened one lovely moonlight evening. It was as
well my mother was not with us for she would never have
allowed me to drink with my father. She was strongly
opposed to wine, while my father greatly enjoyed it. Now
and then this led to a little friction between the two, but
my mother proved good-natured and accommodating on
the whole and did not begrudge my father his jar of rice-
wine at night. When we sat together, a small table with
the wine, two bowls, and a basket of fruit was placed
before him. My mother usually remained with us until it
became late and the jar was empty. That summer evening,
however, she was not with us, because the women were at
their reading circle.

Already the moon had risen over the roof of the empty
school building and gave light to a cloudless night sky.
The wall between the two courtyards cast a hard shadow.
There was nobody to be seen, not a voice to be heard.
Nothing moved in the big house. All life, all conscious-
ness radiated to me from the smiling face of my father,
who could tell such wonderful tales. The longer the evening progressed, the more he drank and the more thrilling
his stories. How many poems he could recite and sing!

"Have you ever heard of the great Korean poet Kim-
Saggaz?" he asked me.

49

"No," I replied in happy expectation of another story.

"His father was an important official, the Governor of a province in the South. His King was a bad ruler and soon fell into disrepute. The powerful Governor in the South commanded thirty thousand archers, all excellent marksmen. With them he marched to Seoul to overthrow the King. Three provinces had already declared for him and there was no one to stop his progress to the North. As he entered at the head of his troops into a newly gained town, he met a man who was waiting for him in the street. The man was unarmed and his hands were empty; yet he ran up to the horse of the victorious conqueror and snatched the bridle."

My father looked into his wine-bowl and emptied it. I tried to fill it again, but the jar was empty.

"Nothing left?" he asked, and as he asked he became a little—I'm not sure whether I may call it that—yes, he became a little sad.

That saddened my heart.

"I'll fetch some more," I said eagerly and stood up with the jar.

He laughed and took hold of my hand.

"You are very bold," he said; "ask your mother as nicely as you can! Perhaps she will let you have a little more!"

"Of course I'll get you some more wine," I replied.

I came back with a full jar and poured for him. He was delighted.

"And who was this opponent?" I asked.

"That is just what I wanted to hear from you. Who could have been so brave?"

I thought for a while and then answered: "The King himself?"

"Well done!" he said, "and it would have been best for the King himself to come and face his enemy unarmed. Perhaps another king might have done it. But this one was a great coward. No, it was not the King, but the son, the conqueror's own son. It was the famous Kim-Saggaz! You didn't expect that, now, did you? But it was really his own son. 'Turn your troops back to the south!' he begged of his father. He, however, replied: 'Become my officer and I will give you a thousand men.' 'No,' said the son; 'you have broken faith with your King and I refuse you my obedience!' With these words he allowed his father to proceed. Kim-Saggaz remained loyal to the King, but did not raise a hand against his father, and became a mendicant poet."

"I should have helped the father," I said when the story was ended.

"No," said my father; "you are too young to understand. Once one has promised allegiance to the King, one may never fail him."

"Kim-Saggaz had promised obedience to his father too, so he could not refuse that."

"That's true," my father admitted, pleased by my logic; "that is why he did not act against his father, but became a poet and left the world."

"I should still have helped my father," I said. I could not comprehend how one could leave one's own father for the sake of the King.

"How pig-headed you are!" my father exclaimed.

51

"No, it only looks like that to you. I do not know whether you, as a grown-up, understand this better than I do!"

"Well spoken! Now then, my clever son, drink a bowl of wine with me!"

He filled the second bowl which stood there empty, just for the sake of etiquette.

The offer threw me into great confusion; hitherto I had looked upon intoxicating drink as an enemy, because my mother spoke against it. Now, however, I did not hesitate long and took up the bowl.

"Now drink!"

I emptied it in one draught. Soon, alas, tears filled my eyes, for the wine was very potent. Quickly my father put a date into my mouth, and I felt better.

"How did you like it?"

"Well," I said.

"There you are, then take another bowl!"

I nodded. Speak I could not. Everything inside me was in turmoil and my throat seemed sealed. Even so, I strove to sit quietly and not to complain while my father recited one poem by Kim-Saggaz after the other.

As we were emptying the second bowl, I already had two dates in my hand. This time it wasn't so bad. Gayly and bravely I chewed my dates. Soon, nevertheless, my head began to swim in strange and unaccountable fashion. Still I did not give in and remained sitting as if all were well.

At this moment my mother came to join us and noticed immediately that something was very wrong with me.

"Quite true; yes, indeed," my father told her. "He has had two bowls of wine."

Mother was appalled; yet she did not say anything and her looks were not severe and angry, but rather ironical.

"May I have one more bowl?" I asked my father.

"For heaven's sake!" my mother burst out and quickly took away the bowl.

"Oh, don't be so cruel," my father begged of her: "a little wine can't do him any harm. I must have a friend in my solitude."

"All right, but just this once," she said and filled the bowls.

Very proudly now I emptied my third. I felt quite grown-up. I was accepted as a friend of my father's, who was so wise a man and could tell such wonderful stories.

"If only, Father, Mother could understand how essential wine is to a poet!"

"Quite so," said my father, while my mother half closed her eyes and gave me a sidelong glance.

I could not tell whether she was admiring me or making fun of me. I did not care—not in the very least! The moon was shining so brightly, the air was full of the scent of the peaches, I was sitting there drinking wine, and was my father's friend!

VIII. *The New Learning*

I HAD often heard of the school for what was called "the New Learning," and since last autumn my parents also had begun to speak of it. This extraordinary Institute, founded only a few years before, was in the northern part of our town, in a building distinguished for its many sparkling panes of glass. The subjects taught there sounded odd. It was rumored that the pupils learned neither the classics, nor script-writing, nor even poetry, but altogether new-fangled sciences introduced from a distant Continent named "West of the Ocean" or Europe. Where this continent was situated or what exactly was its science nobody seemed to have any clear notion. Some said that the school taught advanced arithmetic and obscure occult arts, others even spoke of the science of the earth and the heavens: all were afraid that it would undo and corrupt the children because they would not learn the classics.

My father, who seemed to know much more about the Institute, had formed quite a different opinion. After long consultations with my mother and the whole family, he decided that I should receive lessons there for a year. For a boy of eleven, he explained, I had read enough of the classics. Tsung-yong and Mang-dsa, whose works I had been studying for the past few months, would have to do for the present, and the next books were in any case too difficult for my age.

I felt rather uneasy when I was asked whether I would like to go to this school. Being an only son, I had no wish to be corrupted and, what is more, I enjoyed reading the classics and loved classical poetry. But I trusted my father and said that I would try if that were his wish.

Thus one clear, cold spring morning I followed him out of the house into the town. I was wearing my best suit and carried my lunch in a neat basket given to me by my mother. We walked up our little lane and into the main road. "Is it true," I asked my father, "that we will learn the science of the heavens?"

"That is what people say," he replied. "Listen carefully whenever the heavens are spoken of. It is the highest knowledge."

"Will I be able to understand it?"

He nodded as if to encourage me. "See to it that your heart is always pure," he pronounced, gravely.

We walked across the street of the bell-tower, took one or two turnings, and soon stood at the gate of the big building. This, then, was the formidable, much-talked-of 'new' school, its name inscribed above the entrance. I gave a quick glance into the court, which looked vast.

"Come along," my father called, for he had gone ahead. "You aren't, by any chance, afraid?" he asked when I hesitated.

Slowly I crossed the threshold. Inside the gate I stopped again to look at the many rooms, but he pulled me along by the hand and led me to one of them. An old gentleman came out of the door, and Father told me to make my bow.

"This is the head of the school," he explained with a smile. "Be grateful to him and obedient."

While he was talking to the Principal, I was taken into a sombre and sunless chamber to a young teacher called Song. I bowed deeply to him also, and he invited me to sit down. I asked whether I was to sit on the chair which stood beside his. I had never sat on anything other than mats and a chair struck me as rather too grand. He gave me permission and I took my seat with great care.

"What have you learned so far?" he began to question me and, noticing that I was still too shy to speak, he went on: "Have you read Tung-sam, for instance?"

I nodded. "Up to the eighth volume."

"And what else have you read?"

Once again I sat there, dumb. I could not think, for the moment, what I had read after that. I was too confused.

"Shak, perhaps?" he asked.

I nodded my head.

"Mang-dsa, too?"

I nodded again.

"Have you read Tsung-yong already?"

"Him, too, I have read.."

"That is much." He fetched a book from his case, opened it, and laid it before me. "Have a look at that."

I read.

"Can you understand it all?"

"Yes," I said, though hesitating a little.

"Now what could be the meaning of this word?" he asked, pointing to a character which meant "America".

"Perhaps it might be a country near England," I suggested. I had often heard the two names mentioned in conversation about Europe.

Teacher Song considered for a while and then determined that I was to join the second form.

My father had gone without seeing me again: there was nobody in the Principal's room. He had left me to my fate.

On the first day I learnt nothing about heaven. The natural history lesson was about a ball being pulled apart by four horses. Then we peered into a long glass cylinder where a copper coin and a feather were made to move from one end to the other. There followed an hour of arithmetic. Twice we had gymnastics. Towards evening we were shown a tube; when you lifted it to your eyes, objects inside glittered in a myriad of bright colors.

. . . . .

It was sunset. My class-mates were pouring out of the school gates. I was again called to teacher Song. He gave me two school-books, a satchel, some pencils, and a slate, saying that they had been brought for me by a tradesman. I looked at the books; one was called *The History of the Occident*, the other *Laws of Nature*. I opened them and examined the inside. The natural science book was full of pictures: of scales, a glass cylinder, sailing-boats, and a European steamship. The ball which had been discussed during the day was not there.

Teacher Song asked me whether I had a watch.

"No," I said.

"Has your father one?"

"No."

"That's a pity," he said, with concern. "'Do you know the new reckoning of time?"

"Twelve hours?"

"Yes, but twice twelve hours; twelve before noon and twelve after. Tomorrow you will have to come to school at eight o'clock. Today the sun just touched the wall of the southern playing-field as the clock struck eight. Come in any case right after your morning meal."

I was still searching through the nature book.

"I can't find the ball," I announced eventually.

"Which ball do you mean?"

"The one which is being pulled by four horses."

"For that you will have to ask teacher Ok. I only teach history. But go home now; it is getting dark and your parents will be waiting for you.'

.　　.　　.　　.　　.

In my father's room the men and women of our house were assembled, my mother and my sister among them. They all had a good look at the books, my satchel, and the writing things, while I ate what was left of my father's evening meal.

When the others had gone back to their rooms and my father and I were in bed, he asked me what I had learned.

"Many things, Father."

"Have you heard anything about Europe?"

"Indeed, but it was something very queer."

"Well, then, why don't you tell me what it was?" he said impatiently.

"I can't explain it properly. I listened very carefully, but couldn't quite make out what the teacher said. He explained how a ball was to be pulled apart by four horses. Toward the evening I saw a glass tube. Every stone in the school yard, the clothes of the people, the tiles on the roof, everything shone in many colors as soon as I put the glass to my eyes. I can't understand why that is so. Can you tell me?"

"Did they say that it had come from Europe?" he asked, after a long silence.

"Yes, I think they did."

"Who was the teacher who showed it to you?"

"They called him Ok."

"And what did he say about it?"

"He said that the light was being split, or something."

"Split the light? Split the light?" he repeated in a whisper.

After a while he asked me to light the lamp again and to take some books out of the low case in the corner of the room. These books he had ordered from the capital. They contained much European wisdom. He looked through them all, but then he made me put them back again.

"You must be more attentive at school," he said, disappointed. "Now blow out the lamp and go to sleep."

"I felt so queer today," I said. "Everything at the school was strange. For a long time I was afraid I would never like it there, because it is so different from what I am used to."

My father did not answer at once.

"Were you sad?" he asked at last.

"It must have been that. I could not help thinking of the old school and of home."

"Come into my bed for a while," he said, and I felt his hand drawing me close to him. "Do you remember the song of Sotong-pa?" It was the song of a sailor poet which I had read to him the year before. "Will you recite it to me?"

I did so without hesitating once.

"Could you sing me the song of Eternal Grief?"

I did that too. It took a long time before I was through all the fifty verses.

"Is your heart still now?" he asked.

I nodded and crept back into bed.

"Will you go to school again tomorrow?"

"Yes, if it is your wish, Father."

IX. *The Clock*

NEXT to me at the new school sat a boy called Kisop;
he was bright and good-looking and seemed to know
many answers. He was sorry for me because I understood
but very little and sat rather dejectedly at my desk. Of
natural history I could make almost nothing and of arithmetic even less. From time to time Kisop glanced into my
open copy-book and wrote down a few figures, to give me
the results at least of the difficult problems. This, unfortunately, was of very little use to me, for I had no notion of
how these results might be arrived at. Thus I sat there the
entire day, discouraged and longing for the evening. On
the way home, however, I did my best to get things straight
in my head: little odd bits of natural science and whatever
I had been told about Europe, so as to be able to tell my
father about it. Anything new, however slight, pleased
him. I told him word for word what I had learnt and

brought home everything that looked even faintly European: pieces of paper with European print or writing on them, pictures of the tall houses, the bridges and steeples. Carefully and deliberately he examined them all.

During the breaks and at the end of school hours some of the boys would gather in the play-ground and talk of the countries of Europe and of the profound knowledge of their wise men, whose names I could never remember because they sounded so strangely foreign. Puksori, one of my schoolmates, told of a rich Chinese who once upon a time had visited a European sage. Unnoticed, a valuable diamond ring slipped off the rich man's finger and fell into the courtyard below. When, during the conversation, he became aware of his loss and mentioned it to the sage, he received this answer: "Fear not, honored guest; in a European country no one will take that which does not belong to him"! Down in the courtyard, a servant was sweeping the ground. Looking through the window, the anxious Chinaman saw him pick up the ring and gently replace it as soon as he had brushed the spot where it had fallen.

Kisop told a story of a Chinese prince who had lived in Europe for a time. When he decided to return home, he went to pay his respects to the highest man in the land, to take his leave of him, and to thank him for his country's hospitality. Outside the castle he met a gardener who was weeding the gravel path, and asked him whether he could be received by his master. But the gardener answered thus: "I am myself the President of this country. In Europe we have neither servants nor masters, as the barbarian countries do."

How delighted my father was with this story: "You see," he said to me excitedly, "the Europeans, they are true human beings!"

· · · · ·

The big wall-clock which my father had ordered a few days before struck midnight. Its chime boomed through the whole house; when it had died away, the clock continued her steady tick-tack into the still night.

My father sat by candle-light looking through my school-books. "There is nothing else you have heard about Europe?"

"No."

"Didn't they tell you who governs these countries?"

"No. But I think it must be the Presidents. They speak of them as kings."

"That might be possible."

He went on reading in my books, sometimes pausing to consider, sometimes smiling to himself. Then he put them aside and stared before him, as if intent on peering into a new world which was hidden from him.

· · · · ·

One day, as I was about to go home, a boy stood waiting for me by the school gates. He belonged to a senior form and was called Yongma. "Are you the son of Kamtsal Li who lives within the Southern Gate?" he asked me as I came out.

"Yes," I said, "I am that."

"We are to go together to see a family and try to get their son to join our school."

I had heard that the pupils of the new school went about the town visiting other middle-class families to explain to

63

the parents the advantages of the new education and to persuade them to send their children to our school.

"Teacher Song has chosen us two for tonight," Yongma continued when he noticed my hesitation. "Come along right after your evening meal and meet me by the willow bridge. And don't forget to bring some of your school books. We'll show them to the parents."

Dusk was already falling as we walked along the river. Only the water gleamed in the twilight.

"Do you know anything about Newton?" Yongma asked me on the way.

"No," I had to admit.

"But surely you've heard of the force of gravity, which makes things fall to the ground?"

Yongma looked at me with surprise. He could hardly believe that a boy of my age had never heard of gravity.

"I only know that the earth circles round the sun," I said.

"Good! You can tell the people that," he conceded with a smile. "Or you can speak of oxygen. Tell them that water is composed of two different substances—of oxygen and hydrogen. Our ancestors only knew that the Universe consists of two poles—Yin and Yang—but the Europeans have discovered that this principle applies also to individual things, to the water, the air, and the rocks."

His voice was very gentle, he spoke beautifully and with care.

"Many say that bad times have come over us. Then you must answer them: the times are not bad, it is only that new times have come, like the spring after a long winter with much snow. The azaleas are in bloom and the cuckoo calls. That is how I feel our times."

The father of the family which we were about to visit was a brush-maker. The entire front of his house was covered with huge characters which indicated that writing-brushes were for sale there. As we reached the top of the stone steps, we met a young woman with a watering-can. When she heard what we had come for, she went into the house without a word and locked the door. We knocked repeatedly, but nobody opened. For a while we stood, listening to the rushing water of the little mountain stream nearby, and then we turned back.

"If you can find a wooden box at home," Yongma said, "stick some black paper on it inside and out. One side you must leave open, so that it can be covered with a piece of frosted glass. Make a small hole on the opposite side, no bigger than a needle's head. If you look through the box, you'll see all the trees and flowers reflected on the glass. Show it to your people and tell them that photographs are taken with a box just like that."

When we got to his home, he took me inside to see his many books. Some of them were bound in the European manner and decorated with gilt lettering. I hardly dared to touch them.

"It's only because in Europe they write with gold, while we just use black ink," he told me.

As I was about to leave, Yongma produced a thin book in a blue cover with a European title.

"This is a book which every progressive person ought to read," he said, handing it to me; "show it to your father!"

I ran home as fast as I could.

"Abraham Lincoln, Abraham Lincoln," my father whispered; "is that the name of a man?"

"That is what I took it for, Father."

He read a few pages, glanced through the others and examined the book from all sides. "Go to bed now," he said abruptly, without looking up.

"Is he a European sage?" I asked.

He nodded his head.

"Like Confucius or Meng-tse?"

"No, different."

"Or perhaps like our Yulgok?"

"He's something quite different."

My father's face showed plainly that he did not wish to be disturbed. I kept quiet and waited until he had read the whole book. The story had obviously excited him, but he said nothing to me. He sat in silence, staring at the book before him. Then he lit his pipe and smoked.

Was this European perhaps a poet? A hero, a loyal subject of a bad king? Were there even in Europe kings who governed badly?

I took my pictures from the drawer and examined the tall houses, a wide bridge and a high steeple. I wondered what the steeple might be for?

The clock on the wall struck the hour with its deep, low voice. It sounded as if coming from afar, from the inaccessible seat of wisdom which only now and then sent beams of light through rifts in the clouds.

. . . . .

Since his illness, my father received few visitors. He said

that he needed tranquillity. He gave instructions that all business callers were to be dealt with by Sunpil, the young clerk, and the peasants from our farms received hospitality and advice from Sunok, the bailiff. People came and went, bargained and argued, but only in the outer courtyard that had once been our playground. In the Inner Court, separated from the other by a wall and a gate that could be locked, all remained quiet throughout the day. In the morning a farm-hand swept the ground, and in the evening Kuori watered the flowers.

The only visitor whom my father saw every day was my mother. She came after the evening meal, accompanied by Kuori or one of the other servants, and stayed with us for some time. She discussed the household with my father, told him what went on in the Inner Court, and of the women who had visited her. Then she listened to the news I brought home from school, let down the rolled-up bamboo shutter in front of the open window, lit the lamp, and wished us a good night.

Of my three sisters, Knogi, the eldest, was already married, and the youngest, Setye, was still too shy to enter my father's room. Osini was the only one who came occasionally in the evening to sit with us when we talked. She was very interested in my school and liked to look through my books, even reading a passage here and there with enjoyment. From time to time she would take along a book which I did not need the next day, to study it carefully in her own room. Once, however, when my father asked her whether she, too, would like to go to the new school, she appeared quite frightened and quickly put down the book.

"How can you tease me so!" she said, blushing.

One evening, while I was alone in the little "east room" on the Inner Court, Osini came to see me. "These books are so strange," she began with disapproval. "They contain no classical words and no sentences of any profound meaning. Do you believe that they will one day make you a wise man?"

"I hope so," I answered.

"And what do you learn from these books?" she asked with an air of superiority, fingering one page after another. "I think it is a pity for you. You are, after all, gifted; you have read Tsung-yong. You have learnt many old poems by heart, and have even copied Yulgok's anecdotes. But now, with this new learning, you are wasting yourself on worthless things."

Osini was an intelligent girl. She liked reading and knew many of the anecdotes and novels written in the old style; her speech was rich in classical Korean words unfamiliar even to my mother. People considered her the cleverest of us children, and indeed she was the only one who often found fault with me. She thought my handwriting miserable, my language without beauty or dignity. For this reason I tried to avoid talking with her.

"It is just that the new learning is something different," I told her at last: "it teaches you how to build railways which will enable people to travel over thousands of miles. It teaches you to estimate how far off the moon is, or how to make use of the power of the lightning to produce light."

"That does not make you a wise man," she said with concern.

"These are the new times," I continued, "brighter ones after our long, dark sleep. A fresh breeze has awakened us. Now it is spring, after a long winter. That is what they say."

For a long while Osini seemed lost in thought and hardly listened to me. "And how far is it from us to this country which they call Europe?" she asked me at last.

"That I haven't learned yet, but it must be many times ten thousand miles."

"Once upon a time the Princess Sogun married into a country without any flowers. It couldn't be there, could it?"

"No; that was only the land of the Huns."

"Do you believe they have flowers in Europe like our lilies, forsythias and azaleas?"

"I don't know."

"Do you believe they have a south wind there? Do they sit in the moonlight drinking wine in order to write poems?"

"I cannot tell."

"Then you don't know anything worth knowing," she summed up, disappointed.

X. *Vacations*

AT the old school we had no summer vacations, nor did we have Sundays free either. When it became very hot we learned a little less than usual and were allowed to go bathing more often. Only twice a month there were no lessons.

At the new school the Sundays were holidays, and now in summer we were allowed to be idle for a whole month. It was wonderful. My father was pleased, too, and allowed me to choose whether to go to a famous teacher of classic script who lived in a distant village in order to improve my calligraphy, or to stay at home and copy a classical work. He was disappointed with my handwriting and expected me to employ the holiday making it better. I decided in favor of the latter. I was given several fine brushes and an empty copybook which I had to fill with small letters the size of a grain of rice. Each morning I learned two pages of the text and proceeded to copy them. My father made me repeat many of the characters again and again, and it happened quite often that I had to do over an entire page.

In the afternoons I received instruction in *paduk*, a dignified board game played with numerous black and white counters. I noticed that the exquisite white pieces, of the thinness of paper, were fragments of shells worn away by the sea, with the mother-of-pearl coating still showing on one side. The black ones were squat and round and of slate-grey color. They looked as if they had come from the bottom of a brook.

"Now take up a black stone," said my father, as I examined the pieces, "and set it on the board as firmly as you can."

I did as I was told, and the box that formed our playing-board gave out a clear sound which lingered in the air. The inside of the box was strung with many copper wires, my father explained.

"When your opponent has moved a piece," he told me, "wait until the sound has died away. Only then is the time to make your own move, and let none be unconsidered."

I received a handicap of twenty points and the contest began.

"Slowly!" he called out, when I was about to send my little stone counter too precipitately to what looked like a favorable place. "Always think first. The opponent's weakness is very often only a delusion."

Once he told me that *paduk* was not fit for men to play, but only for the Gods who now and then came down from our mountains to while away their time over this game. "Can you imagine a God playing hastily like children racing with each other?"

"No, the Gods are very dignified," I said.

"Surely you have heard of the woodcutter who lost his

way and strayed into the realm of the Gods, where he
watched them at their game. By the time he returned
home his axe had rotted away. The game of the timeless
Gods had taken too long for the earth-bound human.''

We played on and on. Every afternoon, as soon as the
worst of the heat was over, I had to carry the game into
the garden and set up the board in the shade of a tree.
We would sit on a rattan mat, the game between us.
I always lost, but never ceased to believe that one day I
should succeed in winning. We played until cool shadow
lay over the whole garden and Kuori called us to our
evening meal.

At night I was often fetched by Yongma at the hour
when my mother came to join my father. We still went
occasionally to enlist new pupils for our school; at other
times we just strolled through the town to look at the
shops. Walking along the main streets to the East Gate
gave us the chance to see Japanese stalls.

I knew very little of the Japanese, who in our country
were not quite accepted as civilized and had long been
known by the none-too-flattering name of "Wai barbarians". Yongma, however, said that recently they had learned
much from the Europeans and had reformed their country, so that Japan was now to be counted among the civilized nations. It was a fact that Japanese traders sold many
strange articles which must have come from Europe:
sweets, cigarettes, lamps, oil, dolls, and toys of all sorts.
In front of one of the stalls was a tilted wooden board with
many nails. For a copper coin one was allowed to run a
ball down the incline towards slots which marked a score.

The big prize was a wall clock, and the Japanese dealer called out indefatigably: "Come and play, fetch my wall clock, *arâ arâ arâ*; I must lose my wall clock; my wall clock must go."

Another store sold and rented bicycles. Yongma stayed longer here than anywhere else, making a careful study of them. He reached the conclusion that the cycles really did come from Europe because they looked so strange.

"Why shouldn't I try to ride for once?" he asked me after he had watched the other children for a while.

"It is not exactly dignified," I replied, not quite convinced yet that this striking toy did come from so illustrious a place as Europe; "after all, you do belong to an educated family."

He nodded, gave it a little more thought, and abandoned the idea.

Until late at night all the stalls and booths were brightly lit. The salesmen were sitting on mats in front of their wares. In contrast to our countrymen, they wore black. The black material of their clothes often had white patterns like snowflakes or plain lines and dots. On their backs many even had large Japanese characters, which looked terribly gross. Not one was dressed in elegant white and not one wore shoes. All went about in clattering sandals with their toes turned inwards. Japanese women were also among the stalls selling goods; they were not carried in litters and they allowed themselves to be seen in the street unaccompanied by a servant, as if they were but servants themselves. We wondered whether all these people belonged to a dishonored caste or if they were just so poor that they had to send their women out into the streets like serving-maids.

I had never seen any pictures of the country from which these people came, neither of their villages nor of their cities. Even Yongma did not know much about them; he merely repeated that Japan was now reformed and had many trains and steamers.

"People say that there are now six civilized nations in the world," he told me once: "England, America, France, Germany, Russia and Japan. Japan, it is true, comes at the very end; for it has, after all, only imitated the others."

"And where does our country stand?" I asked with astonishment.

"Not among the civilized by a long shot," was his dejected reply, "because we still have too few railways."

"And China?" I asked.

"The Chinese seem to be very conservative," he replied after a long silence. "Yu, the cloth vendor, was very angry once when I suggested that he should have his hair cut because a pigtail is so old-fashioned. The old man flew into a rage and would certainly have boxed my ears, if I had not run away as fast as I could. The green-grocer behind the Namsan mountain is very old-fashioned too. Once I showed him my school books to find out how much he understood. I wrote in Chinese characters the question whether China would introduce European culture. He laughed and dismissed the idea with a sweep of his hand. Then he wrote on the ground with the bowl of his pipe: 'Europe is a land of barbarians. They have no Confucian morals.'"

74

The word "conservative" did not sound good. I thought it must mean something like stupid and obstinate. I was sorry for the Chinese, if they really were conservative, for to me China meant beauty, tenderness, and splendor. Only to think of the sound of the words "Yang Tse Kiang," "Tung Ting Hoo," "Suchow," or "Hangchow," or to repeat a few verses of "Sutung Po" or "Tao Yen Ming" was to see a splendid world opening out before me.

Setye and Osini, my sisters who had read many Chinese novels, thought and felt the same way. Although they had never seen the morning fog clear from the Yangtse valley, nor the moonlight over the Yoang groves, they loved the splendid Land of the Central Empire above all others, better even than our own homeland, which, with a faint tinge of disdain, they often referred to as "that little Eastern country."

. . . . .

Towards the end of the summer holidays we had a strange and eventful night. After our evening meal I was fetched by Kisop and another school friend with the terrible name of Horang, which means tiger-wolf. They told me to come with them to our school at once; there was to be a march through the streets because today was the birthday of the King or the Queen or of some other prominent person.

When we arrived at the school, the pupils—some two hundred, perhaps—were already assembled in the courtyard. In time the gymnastics teacher arrived and lined us up in four rows, according to size. Yongma was in front, for he was the tallest of us all, while I stood almost at the very end of the whole column, next to Kisop. We were addressed at length and admonished to march through the streets in perfect order so that the citizens of our town and the pupils of other schools should have reason to admire us.

When dusk fell, each one of us received a colored paper lantern with a burning candle. Then we were off through the school gates, with drums and trumpets, singing patriotic songs. We marched to the Bell Yard. From the south and east came other groups of scholars, also on their way to the same place, singing and carrying lanterns. Two more "new schools" had been created that summer. Kisop explained that one of them was founded by Christian missionaries.

Now all three schools were joined together, and we marched backwards and forwards across the town until at last, after passing through the Three Gates, we came to the Governor's Palace, with its infinity of courtyards. It made a veritable sea of splendid lights.

I fell into a most solemn mood. Many festive gatherings had taken place here in earlier days, but I had never advanced farther than into the outer yard, through a slit of a side door. From there I had admired the glory of the light in the other courts and listened to the lovely music. This time our procession moved boldly through the imposing Three Gates, past many halls, and to the Courtyard of the Lotus Pavilion, where we were received by the Governor himself.

We stood around the big lotus-pond, drawn up to form the shape of a plum blossom, the emblem of our Royal

Family. The light of countless paper lanterns was mirrored and reflected in the water. At that moment the most important man in our province appeared before the pavilion.

The Governor praised our sound judgement in recognizing so promptly the new times. Our homeland, he said, was a small nation, but our ancestors had developed a high degree of civilization and had passed it on to Japan. Now it was Japan which moved ahead and wished to help us reform our country; for this reason, we should strive hard to reach the same heights as the brother nation farther in the east.

Enthusiastically we greeted our homeland and our King with the traditional cheers of *"Manse! Manse!"*

At the end of the ceremony each of us received a batch of pencils and two copybooks as rewards for this demonstration of belief and interest in the new civilization.

We returned home content with ourselves. I thought it a wonderful evening. True, we were a small nation and lived in a small country—but our wisdom was more important than that. Big, glorious China had once called us "Little China," because our ancestors were so wise. And who but we had given Japan her writing, her philosophy, her religion, her architecture, and heaven knows what else! Now we were lagging behind Japan in acquiring the new civilization; but what harm was there in that? After all, we were wise—the Governor himself had said it. We were all uplifted by his words.

I thought it a really wonderful evening!

XI. *On the Okke River*

IN the autumn school took up more time, for now we
studied geography and what was called world history;
our lessons, moreover, had to be copied laboriously from
a blackboard for lack of text-books. Often it was already
cool when I left the school gate behind me in the half-light
of the evening.

It was on one such late afternoon that I was fetched by
Kuori, our maid. She had been sent by my mother because,
so she said, it was dangerous to be alone in the streets
today. Many Japanese soldiers were about the town, and
some had even forced their way into private houses.

I felt uneasy, although I had often heard that the Japanese had come to us not as enemies, but as friends and to
help us. We hurried home. When I heard Japanese soldiers spoken of, I was always rather frightened.

"What does my father say?" I asked Kuori.

"I don't know."

"And what does Mother say?"

"That there will soon be war again."

"And Sunok?"

"That this will be the end of the world."

We hurried on. Agape against the dark night sky stood the large south entrance to the city. The High Street was darker than usual. The fruit-vendors had abandoned the stalls where on other days they sold melons, pumpkins, pears, and pies by the light of their paper lanterns. The pie-man with his beautiful haunting tunes had made off too.

At home the events of the day were the subject of excited discussion. It was true that soldiers had turned up in every street and lane to search houses. Sunok had seen three soldiers forcing their way into the Bread House at the top of the main street. Nobody knew what they were looking for, because it was impossible to understand their speech, and no one was allowed to go near them. The general feeling was that something terrible awaited our town.

My parents conferred late into the night. My mother proposed that at least some of the children—Osini especially, who was already grown up, and I, as the youngest—should be taken to safety. My father would not consent, though he did not understand the significance of the searches any better. There was no reason, he said, to fear war, and the soldiers would do no harm to innocent citizens. We should offer no resistance and give up whatever they wanted. The soldiers were certain to have been sent by our King himself for some good reason.

My mother found it hard to regain her composure after

79

such a day of excitement, but she gave way with a heavy heart, and in the end only directed that I was not to leave the house for the next few days and should sleep in my old east room on the Inner Court. I obeyed her willingly, although I was no longer afraid now that my father had entirely dispelled my fears.

The next afternoon four soldiers armed with rifles actually did come to our house. They walked through all the courtyards, pried into every room and shed, and then left again as my father had foretold, without molesting us or taking anything. After that we all calmed down and I was allowed to go to school again. Only Osini, who had fled from courtyard to courtyard at the very sight of the soldiers, was upset and scared for weeks to come.

Such house-searches were repeated often, almost every day or even twice a day. Occasionally the soldiers appeared early in the morning; sometimes they turned up unexpectedly in the Inner Court during the evening and caused the women to run away in terror.

At the same time a sinister rumor was about: it was said that some of our countrymen—young peasants, hunters, and others opposed to the new times and suspecting the Japanese of evil intentions—had gathered in the nearby mountains to fight the invaders. This would explain the recurrent searches in our town for hidden arms.

At first my father took all of this for mere gossip. Yet there seemed to be truth in the story, for we saw more and more heavily armed Japanese troops pass through the West and the North Gates. They marched out singing and singing they returned to the town.

Later they brought prisoners. It was a terrible sight, terrible to watch our own peasants being dragged through the streets, beaten bloody and in heavy manacles, their features swollen and appallingly mutilated. Never had I seen a human being in chains nor one so flayed. I staggered home sick with fear and horror and a cold sweat ran down my face.

My mother again proposed that I should be taken away from school in order to go to a more peaceful part of the country. I was a young child, she argued, and ought to be spared such impressions. Father discussed the matter at length but in the end did not consent. He only sent Pang the laborer and our bailiff to the peasants on our farms; they were to warn our people not to get involved in any trouble with the Japanese. As for me, he said I should simply not look at the marching soldiers. Only an uneducated child could be so inquisitive as to stare into their faces.

The fighting became still more violent. Throughout winter and spring prisoners were brought into the town. Even women were among them.

Not until summer, with the onset of the rains, did things begin to settle down at last. The house-searches ceased altogether. Steadily the monsoon rains fell from morning till night.

One evening Kisop came to see me. He looked pale and wan. "Have you heard?" he asked me.

"No; what do you mean?"

He kept me waiting for a while. "I think we have been tricked after all," he said at last; "our country has been annexed."

"By Japan?"

"Of course by Japan."

"Where did you see that?"

"If you have time you can go to the South Gate later and read the proclamation. But be careful. A soldier is there. You must not make any fuss or tear down the poster."

After our evening meal I went to the South Gate accompanied by Kuori. There it was, a large printed manifesto illuminated by two big lamps. All around was still as the grave. Not a soul was to be seen near the gate or in the main street. Only two lights flickered in the darkness, and a soldier with a rifle stood beside the proclamation. I approached cautiously and saw impressed on it a large royal seal.

Yes, it was a letter from the King, the first and last I ever saw in my life. It touched my heart, for it was a parting letter—the parting letter of a whole race of kings who had given us their protection for half a millennium. When I had read it all, Kuori came up to me and pulled me out of the archway.

"What does it say?" she asked me. She was unable to read.

"Our King has gone away!"

"Forever?"

"Yes, forever."

"Why has he gone away?"

"I don't know."

At home I repeated to my father the text of the proclamation word for word.

He listened attentively, but made no comment.

"Is there still worse to come?" I asked him.

82

He only looked at me in silence.

Everyone in the house was silent, the men in the outer courtyard, my mother, my sisters—all were silent.

Late into the night my parents and Sunok sat over a jar of wine and spoke of the kings of the last dynasty. In the end my father came to the conclusion that the whole Royal Family had become too weak to protect us. Now we should have to wait patiently for a new king to come and rule over us. To me he said that I should go to my school unafraid and take no notice of worldly matters.

· · · · ·

Before autumn was over they began to pull down the town walls, the town gates, and the official palaces, and to widen the narrow streets. Shops were dismantled, houses and courtyards broken up. Newly exposed heating-shafts peered through the rubble-heaps, and with difficulty I made my way to and from school across what were once our streets. Day and night the work went feverishly on. From all directions came the heavy crash of the battering-ram, the sharp bang of the hammer, and shrill whining of the saw; thick dust filled the air. Men shouted, gave orders, gesticulated, and quarreled. I was glad when our gate closed behind me.

But even our outer courtyard had been affected by this unrest. Incessantly people came and went. Expelled peasants, dismissed officials, refugees, and emigrants adrift across the country came to ask for shelter. Sunok offered them hospitality only for a few hours and then sent them on their way again. He had to explain the whole day long that our house was not as wealthy as it looked and that they should try their luck elsewhere. This went on throughout the long, cold winter. More and more beggars and refugees arrived to fill all the guest-rooms; Sunok sat in front of the house cross and full of bitter words: "Oh, these miserable times, this miserable world!"

Only the Fountain Court remained quiet; indeed it was more quiet than ever. The whole day long my father, with the help of an interpreter, was involved in discussions with the occupation authorities over the countless new regulations or the new taxes, and this so exhausted him that quite early in the evening he had to lie down and could not stand very much conversation. When I told him about my school he only listened for a short while and then asked me to lie down myself and to blow out the lamp because he was in need of rest. Quite often he interrupted me saying: "Enough of that now; go for a walk and come back to me later."

I felt I was becoming tiresome to him and held my tongue.

I did not care to go for a walk. The dismantled town walls, the unroofed tower gates filled my mind at night with unspeakable sadness and great terror. I preferred to stay at home. When I was with my father, I still felt somehow protected. I was his flesh and blood, he would surely be able to look after me.

. . . . .

Summer returned. One hot afternoon my father asked whether I would like to go with him to the Okke valley to bathe. I was delighted. The Okke was a fine, small river in a quiet valley full of old trees. In their shadow I had spent many days of my childhood while I was still at the old school.

Kuori preceded us with a mat and a small tray of fruit and wine, while I with the *paduk* board under my arm followed my father. Outside the town we took the familiar path along the brook and gradually climbed through the defile to the mountain farm where the old pavilion stood. Kuori had already prepared our seats and left.

While my father looked around the countryside, I set up the *paduk* game and covered the squares with black handicap stones.

"Nothing has changed here during all these years," my father said with a smile. "Don't you feel that this is a world of its own?"

"Yes, that is so, Father," I replied. No human sound was heard, only the chirping of the cicadas from the treetops, and from the ravine the steady murmur of the brook. All the stillness of the day seemed to repose in the deep green shadow, broken once in a while by a cool mountain breeze.

I filled my father's bowl. "May you live a thousand years!" I said, repeating the salutation of the Singers.

He smiled. "Have you ever tried to sing a Shidso song?"

"No, how could I?"

"Try," he said and sang the song of the 'Mild South Wind.' It was a sombre ancient melody, usually presented by famous singers as a wine song. Speechless with admiration I listened, for I had never known he could sing so beautifully. For myself, I could not summon up the courage to follow his example. He looked at the games board. "Still ten points handicap?" he asked with a frown.

Reluctantly I took away two corner stones and only held the inner wall occupied with my pieces.

He took away another two counters. "Surely you can beat your own father with a handicap of six," he laughed and moved his first piece.

Naturally I lost the game.

"Well then, make it eight points!"

I lost again.

He looked at me with pity. "You have lost practice. There is nothing to be done but to give you two more pieces!"

"I don't mind," I said and continued playing with ten points.

"Let's stop playing," he suddenly said when he found that I put my pieces all too often on the wrong spot. "Take off your clothes and get into the water for a while."

I was sorry to have disappointed him. "You must remember that a tiger sometimes gives birth to a dog," I said to console him.

"Never mind; come closer and let me have a look at you! Stand straight; you need not be embarrassed before your father."

He looked at me from all sides. "You are still very skinny," he concluded with real concern. "How old are you?"

"Thirteen."

"Well, there is time. Now go slowly into the water. It is extremely cold here."

He took a bowl of wine and watched me wading clumsily from one rock to the next.

Then he came into the water. He seated himself cautiously under the edge of a big broad rock and let the water trickle over his shoulder. He had hardly been there for a minute when abruptly he leapt out again and sank into the sand, seized by a sudden spasm. He was deadly pale and shook all over. Quickly I got a towel and rubbed him, because I believed he was cold.

Gradually his face regained color and he got up again.

"What happened, Father?"

"Nothing, nothing has happened at all. Just fetch me my clothes."

We dressed, but the shock still made me shiver.

My father, however, said to me: "Don't be afraid; I shall live for a long time yet. I will live until after you marry a beautiful wife and present me with a grandchild."

But for me all the joy of living had been drained away. "Father, please let us go home."

"No, no," he said with a laugh, "you can see that I am quite well again. Let us stay for a while in this beautiful spot."

He looked at the mountains, still aglow in the evening sun. The farm itself was already lost in shadow and from the valley rose a cool wind.

"Will you try one more game?"

"No, please let us go home."

Fortunately, Kuori soon came to fetch us back.

"The life-force wells up unbroken from this brook," he said as we left; "take care if ever you bathe here again."

Hardly had he crossed the threshold of our house when

he was taken with a new spasm. He had to be carried unconscious into my mother's room.

The whole evening I raced from doctor to doctor.

Shortly before midnight my mother told me to kneel on Father's left and to take his hand into mine. She took his right hand and began to pray. We all joined in, while Kuori spread out a broad white cloth on the floor to prepare a way for his soul from the bed to the threshold of the house.

XII. *Years of Mourning*

O SINI had become very silent. She did not speak as often or as much as she used to. My father's death seemed to have changed her much. Silently she went about her jobs in the Inner Court, and it was only rarely that she entered Father's room, where she had appeared each day in his lifetime, despite my mother's admonition that she should not go so often to the men. Only when my mother had gone on her usual autumn journey and Osini had to take her place, would she come late at night into my room to see whether everything was in order. She watched me drawing and writing for a while, but without asking what I might be drawing and without criticizing my handwriting. "Go to sleep soon," she said softly. "Mother would wish it."

Often I pored over my books until past midnight. My studies were more difficult and consumed more time than of old, for we had to learn a great deal of Japanese, and all our textbooks had been replaced by others written in the Japanese language. History was to be re-learnt altogether; all events which had happened in the time of Korean independence were eliminated because the Korean people were no longer looked upon as a nation with its own history, but rather as an outlying community which should always have paid tribute to the Japanese Empire.

Other subjects, like geography and natural science, also demanded harder work, on account of the many changes in terminology and in the arrangement of the syllabus. The teaching of these subjects had been much curtailed in favor of Japanese language lessons; there was no time for them. Without much explanation or comment, we were taken perfunctorily through the curriculum such as we found it in our text-books. All the rest was left to the pupils themselves.

Of my school friends, Kisop was one who came often to talk with me for a while or to help me with my homework. He was often ailing and from time to time could not go to school for weeks on end. Even so he was still one of the best pupils in my form and never tired of lending me a hand in mathematics. He would sit down beside me and watch me solving the problems. Whenever I made a mistake he would correct me with a gentle smile, but without uttering one word.

Yongma arrived each night, but never for more than a few minutes, to ask invariably whether there was anything I had failed to understand at school. He was better able to help me than any of the others because he was the most clever and experienced of us all and knew more Japanese. He answered every question concisely and clearly and then went off again immediately, for there were many others in equal need of his help and he also had his own work to do.

Mansu, too, came to join us. For the past year he had sat close to me in our classroom and had become a friend.

He talked a good deal and often told me of his walks and of the strange old trees in the neighborhood of our town, of the lovely bathing-places in the mountain brooks and of the little temples and pagodas which he had newly discovered. Learning came easily to him and he understood many facts of natural science more quickly than I did, so that he was often able to help me.

Despite all my friends' assistance I had to work much harder than the others to keep pace. I could not tell whether the real reason was that I had been taught too long at the old school and was not yet accustomed to thinking in the new scientific way. A great deal I did not understand at all, and concepts like atom, ion, and energy meant very little to me. Now algebra was added to the rest, and it caused me a great deal of trouble. Equations were unintelligible to me, and I failed to see the purpose of the whole thing. Neither Mansu nor Kisop were able to explain it, and even Yongma had little to say except that these equations would be useful later in the study of higher physics. I pondered and brooded over them by myself, sometimes deep into the night.

As I sat late over my books, my mother would enter the room and gently take brush or pencil out of my hands, close my books and fold away my papers, and tell me to go to sleep. When I objected that my work was not yet done she would say quite briefly: "That is not necessary; do as I tell you."

One such night she stayed with me me for a while even after I had gone to lie down. "What is it that gives you so much difficulty in your studies?" she asked me.

"Everything—," I mumbled, "mathematics, physics, chemistry; none of it is clear to me yet."

"Don't be sad," she said after a long silence, "if you are not sufficiently gifted for this school. This new civilization, which is so alien to us all, just does not suit you. Think of the earlier years. How easily you learnt the old classics and the poets. There you always shone. Come, leave the new school which torments you and go this autumn to Song-nim farm to recover. It is the smallest of our estates, but the one I like best. Chestnuts and persimmons grow there. Have a good rest, get to know our peasants and their work. You will grow strong in this quiet village and fitter than in this restless town. You are, after all, a child of the old times."

This made me sad. I had always been afraid that my true bent was not towards the new sciences which my father had placed before me because nothing else would lead us to higher culture. To have to give it up after four years of working diligently, just because I was not gifted enough, made me very sad.

"Will you do it?" my mother asked as I lay on my mat in silence.

"Naturally, Mother, I will do as you wish," I said dejectedly.

"My dear child," she said and left the room.

XIII. *At Songnim Bay*

THE little village of Songnim was near a remote and solitary bay distinguished only for its oyster-beds. Along the coast, and hidden deep behind the bay, stood some twenty straw-covered farmhouses. During the day hardly anyone was to be seen about the village, for all the men and women were at work in the fields on the far side of the hills. This was the time of harvesting barley, wheat. and maize. I strolled about from field to field and watched the cutting of the corn and the binding of the sheaves until load after load had been taken back to the farm in ox-carts.

At night I returned to my room, the guest-chamber in the house of the local headman. It was a simple room with walls of loam and only a small rough-hewn wooden table in one corner. For a short period the whole village would come alive. Cows were lowing, and out of the houses came the shouts of mothers calling their children home from the beach for their evening meal. Soon all was quiet again

and the whole village seemed to fall asleep. Only the headman stayed in my room to talk to me for a while. He
found the warmest spot in the room and prevailed on me
to lie down and rest there. He himself sat by the rush-
light to plait a straw rope which, he explained, would be
needed to repair his thatched roof in the autumn. The
lamp was a coarse pottery cup filled with clear vegetable
oil and a wick unable to produce more than a very weak
flame. The monotonous rustle of the straw and the heat
in the room as I lay on my mat would often send me to
sleep against my will. When I woke again the light was
most often out and the Toldari uncle, as I called him, had
gone. Silence lay over the whole house and over the whole
village; only the night tide rolled and splashed in the bay.

. . . . .

When there was no important harvesting to be done, I
did not trouble to watch the workers, and went fishing
instead. I greatly enjoyed this, for it made a delightful
change from the routine work in the fields. Fishing-rod in
hand and basket on arm, I walked along the beach right
to the entrance of the bay, to the oyster-rocks, which even
at low tide were covered by the sea. Sitting on a rock I
could fish undisturbed until the tide came up again. Every
day the headman told me exactly when to leave the rocks
and walk back along the beach without the risk of being
overtaken by the rising water.

There I sat by myself fishing the whole day long. The
so-called "line fish" were the most common fish to take
the bait; they were no more than a finger's thickness and
did not taste particularly good. Only rarely did I catch any-

thing better, and throughout that autumn I never saw a single one of the sea-breams which the peasants fancied so much. Nevertheless I returned day by day to sit patiently on my rock, not just because I enjoyed fishing, but for the wonderful view, which did me so much good. Here I escaped the enclosed bay and the sea spread before me into the infinite. On the horizon water and heavens seemed to melt into each other. In the west the solitary rocky Yenpin Island reached into the autumn sky, and to the north a narrow sandy strip around a low chain of hills lost itself in the distance. Far and wide not a sail was to be seen; a cool breeze now and then played over the wet oyster-rocks.

The peasants never went angling, even though fishing-tackle was to be found in every house. They caught their fish with nets which were laid out beyond the bay near the Main Creek. The haul did not consist of small "line fish," but of quite different and bigger ones, such as flounders, soles, bream, or the long white sword-fish which were highly thought of. Since I had never seen net-fishing before nor ever watched the nets in use, I eagerly accepted an invitation to come along one day when they were to be put out. The peasants had picked on a low night-tide. This at first made me somewhat apprehensive, but I soon learnt that it was just at night that the best fish were caught in the nets.

It was dark along the shoals as we went out, for the moon was not up, and the shallow water through which we waded was bitingly cold. Presently, in the brilliance of the starlit sky, the sea grew luminous. By and by I was able to make out sea-weed and crawling crabs against the background of the dark sea-bed. We crossed endless sand creeks through which at this time the water was still seeping out towards the sea. After much wading we reached the main creek, an immense mass of churning water. Quite close the net was set up like a screen in the form of a horse-shoe. Now and then a big fish as long as my arm would leap out of the water in a vain attempt to jump over the net. The farther the tide ebbed away the more desperate became the attempt of the hard-pressed fish to escape their fate. In mad confusion they thrashed about, leaping in greater frenzy than ever, until at last they found themselves flat at the bottom of the drained sea-bed, shining like quick-silver under the night sky.

Swiftly we gathered them into our baskets and made for home. A deep calm now lay over the shoals, for the surf of the breaking waves had receded. Now and again from the distance faint sounds reached us of people talking or shouting to each other. Probably they were other fishing parties returning with their catch, but we could not see them. One might have taken them for the spirits of the drowned, stalking the seashore and whispering to each other because the night was so beautiful and so still.

The fine autumn weather held. Threshing continued from early morning until late into the evening. Linseed, beans, buckwheat, and beet were brought in, and finally we had the rice harvest. As for the corn, the peasants, after cleaning the ears of the chaff with the help of a draught of artificial wind, filled them into straw sacks holding several bushels each. The headman took me to one farm-house after another and explained not only every aspect of the work but also the difference in quality of the various varieties of corn.

The Toldari uncle tried hard not to let me feel lonely in his village. So that I should have something to read during the evening when there was nothing else to do, he had placed several hand-written books in my room. There were four of them: a slender volume of poems, a collection of anecdotes, and two fat novels. The dark-brown oiled paper of all these books turned out to be so much fingered and worn that I could barely decipher the tiny characters by the weak light of my lamp.

"It is very quiet for you here," he said one day as he fetched me from a farm-house, "because you have lived in town until now. But remember the wise men of other times who retired to the mountains when evil ways came over the world. In daytime they stood behind the plough, and took up their writing brushes only at night. So you, too, must live here quietly until the barbarians go away again and the good old days return."

All the men and women of this peasant village believed that the good old days would return quite soon—as soon as a new Royal Family appeared to rule over our country. I was not able to share this view, yet I never said anything against it, because I could not myself imagine anything better for our people. Moreover, I should have thought it impolite to contradict adults whom I called uncle and aunt. It was an old-established custom for the landlord's family and their peasants to regard each other as relatives and to address each other thus. I liked the custom, and always used to add the name of each farm in order to distinguish between my many uncles and aunts. Thus one was called the Udgel uncle and his wife the Udgel aunt, another the Tuissem uncle and his wife the Tuissem aunt. I went generally by the name of "the nephew from town" and was treated like a real nephew. The headman told me that the custom was a good one because it made the peasants feel truly part of the family. All together formed one big clan headed by the landlord's family who might fittingly be richer than any of the others.

Autumn had gone and snow began to fall. Day and night the wind tossed big white flakes across the bay, the fields, and the roads. The harvest was over, and after the Thanksgiving Prayer the storehouse was made fast with a big padlock. The roofs had a new thatch and new silk paper covered the windows. The peasants now stayed in their warm rooms occupied with their home crafts. They made ropes, cords, plaited mats, nets, and sandals. The women spun and wove and the children were sent out to the village teacher, who also was a peasant and only called the children together in winter to teach them reading and writing.

Now and then neighbors forgathered with their work to gossip or to take turns in reading aloud. The books read were usually novels of the old style concerned with a hero in distress. Maligned and ostracized, he had to leave his homeland and tramp from place to place, enduring hunger and cold, until at last he came to a wise hermit who gave him shelter. In the end the hero himself became a philosopher and was called to the Court, where the King made him a powerful man. He married a beautiful prudent

98

woman and returned home again, where, admired and respected by all who knew him, he lived happily ever after. All novels began and ended like that. This did not prevent them from being read over and over again, and each time the patient audience was roused anew to anger about the unhappy fate which befell intrepid innocence. The effect of the story was heightened by the solemn and half-chanting manner of reciting the novel, which called into play the whole range of voice and mood, now gay and then again melancholy. The deeper the snow and the stiller the night, the more full of pathos the readings, so that you could guess from afar just how serious was the plight of the hero. I often stopped in front of such a house and listened, not to discover how the tale might go on, but just to hear this tone of voice, which reminded me of my own carefree childhood when peace was over our country.

XIV. *Spring*

I N winter I often thought of my school years, of my former school friends, and of everything they had told me
about the new world of Europe. I recalled the pictures I
had collected as a child of the glorious houses and castles
so tall that they belonged to the regions of heaven rather
than to the earth. As I walked along the bay almost
blinded by the driving snow, my imagination would con-
jure up all these buildings in the distant West and the gay,
tall, blond people who lived in them. They knew no
earthly cares, no struggle for existence, and no vice. They
pursued the paths of wisdom and devoted their lives to
investigations into Nature and the cosmos. If one was to
become a truly educated human being of the new civilization, it was in the West that one would have to study.
There one would see everything for oneself, experience
everything oneself, and receive all the new learning from
those who themselves had discovered it. Many beautiful
sagas and anecdotes which I had heard of this wonderful
world came alive again, and I began to consider how I
could get there.

The snow-storms had now ceased. The ice-blocks in the
bay broke loose, and soon they were gone. It became
warmer.

One fine afternoon in March I sallied forth, bound for Shinmak. Shinmak, situated two full walking days from our village, was a small market town through which the railway was said to pass. If I were to board a train there, I would be able to cross the northern frontier of our country, and would surely find opportunities of making my way farther and farther west, until I was bound to arrive in Europe at last. That was all I knew for the time being. What a railway train looked like and how one boarded it, what kind of language one used to make oneself understood abroad or whether people in Europe used money— of all that I knew nothing.

I walked all afternoon and even through the night, for it was easy to find the way in the moonlight. I had to walk throughout the next day, too, till dusk, before I caught my first glimpse of the town far out in the plains. Even from the distance I could see that it was a place very different from our own town, noisy, bustling, and busy. All the best houses on the main street were occupied by Japanese. Their clattering sandals made me quite restless. Screeching, blowing their horns, and ringing their bells, rickshas, motor-cars, and bicycles plunged through dense crowds of pedestrians. With no little trouble I made my way through the throng to the railway station at the far end of the town, only to learn that the next train for Manchuria would not come through until early the following morning.

I tried to acquaint myself thoroughly with the railway buildings and the sidings, the like of which I had never seen before, and took careful note of the entrance and exit, so that I should not go wrong next morning. After a long search I found a bed in a native hostelry on the outskirts of the town. For the first time in my life I spent the night at an inn. Since I intended to rise very early, I went to sleep immediately after the evening meal. My fatigue was great, for I had been walking throughout the previous night without respite.

Although exhausted, I found no real rest. My legs hurt, and in my half-slumber the image of my mother forced itself upon me again and again. I had left a brief parting letter for her on the little writing-desk, so that she should not look for me in vain. I had to do this, for she considered me unpractical and would not have let me go. The thought of the letter had calmed me on my way and had made me almost forget my mother. Now I saw her before me most of the time as if she were really there. At last I fell into fitful sleep, but woke myself within a few minutes, dozed off and woke up again. I heard my mother calling for me and saw her sitting over my letter sadly and at a loss for words. Once she took my face into her two hands and smiled as she used to do whenever she came to Songnim to visit me for a few days. Thus it went on the whole night through.

I dreamt of my childhood. I sat on a straw pillow in our outer court and watched my mother coming out to hang up newly dyed silk cloth. The warmth of the sun filled the whole courtyard. I was thrilled to see my mother, ran up to her, embraced her from behind, and called out:

"Guess, Mother, who is behind you?"

She finished hanging her piece of silk, turned round, and lifted me to her breast.

"Now who could that be?" she laughed, holding me high over her face. "Yes, who is this? My golden bough, my jade leaf! Will you be one day a great poet or a great painter, a hero or the governor of our province?"

Towards dawn I saw her crying bitterly; my head was in her lap. I was upset and whispered: "No, dear Mother, I shall not go away!" I had only seen her weeping once before, and that was when we had come down from the high mountains after my father's funeral, to spend the night in a tent outside the house of the gravekeeper. When I woke again I felt feverish and cold in turn.

Dawn was now breaking, and outside a stinging wind blew across the plains. The small white-washed station hall was brightly lit and crowded with people. Most of them were Japanese, soldiers as well as women, standing about, saluting each other with their repeated deep bows. When finally the little office opened and the railway tickets were being sold, all the uniformed passengers arranged themselves at the head of the queue in order of rank. Next followed those in civilian clothes and sandals. I took my place at the tail of the queue, and when my turn came received a ticket to the capital of Manchuria.

Mist still enveloped the sidings. The ice-cold wind chilled the waiting crowd. At long last the train arrived, thundering, whistling, and smoking. All the passengers raced up to the carriages and pushed through the doors. In no time the whistle sounded and the train departed again, while I was left standing on the platform.

A railway official came up to ask why I had not boarded the train. When I could give him no reason, he took the ticket out of my hand and inspected it. "All the way to Mukden!" he exclaimed with astonishment and cast me a testy glance. Then he led me to the office and told his colleagues.

One of the older men demanded my name and age. "Have your parents consented to this journey to Mukden?" he asked suspiciously.

"No," I said.

"I thought so," he said, becoming sharp. "What did you want to do in Manchuria?"

"Go on to Europe," I answered, hesitating a little.

For some time he looked me searchingly full in the face. "That far you wanted to travel? And have you got a passport?"

"No; I never thought of such a thing."

"Well—and what about luggage?"

"I haven't got any."

"Do you speak English, or French, or German?"

"No, I haven't had time for it yet."

"How much money have you? Show it to me."

I put all my money on the table. He ran his eye over it and grinned. "So you expected to travel to Europe without luggage, without knowing English, without passport, and with so little money?"

"Yes, that is so."

He looked at me askance. "But why, then, didn't you get on to the train?"

I had no answer to that. The young official who had led me back interjected that this was the question I had not been able to answer from the outset.

"Tell me, then, why didn't you get on that train?" the older man asked me once more.

"It was too restless, too noisy, and in too much of a hurry," I replied.

The younger man sneered and said that he had heard the same thing before from Koreans. "The railway is not dignified enough for these people, too noisy and too fast," he remarked, and everybody laughed.

"But you can't very well travel to Europe on an ass," the old man said.

"No, that wouldn't be so easy," I had to admit.

"Will you try again tomorrow, to travel to Europe by our train? Once again, despite the noise?"

"I haven't made up my mind yet."

That was the end of our conversation. The official took back my ticket, paid me the money, and laid it with the rest of my belongings.

"Now go back home and continue your studies. In our country the schools are no worse than in Europe. If you are gifted and can leave the school at the top of your form or somewhere near it you may go to Seoul later and study at the university. Our universities are no worse than the European ones, and Seoul is full of the new civilization. All the public buildings are built in the European style, on three stories, sometimes on four, and the professors are dressed in noble European suits. Remember, though, that you may travel to Seoul only if your parents let you. If I stick to the regulations here I must arrest every runaway like you and send him home in police custody. With you I will make an exception, because you don't look like a bad boy to me. Take your money and go home. But be careful with it, for it is something most precious."

I returned to the inn and went to sleep. I did not wake again until the late afternoon. There was not a ray of sunshine in my room and I felt very cold. Even now the noise from the street outside disturbed me strangely. Coolies drawing rickshas were yelling, bicycle bells were ringing and the street traders shouted out their wares, especially the famous Japanese life-pills, *intan*. From the distance came the whistle of a train steaming into the railway station. There were screams and orders. A second train came from another direction with a deafening roar. Somewhere a policeman was beating a man; one could not avoid hearing his moans and cries for mercy. Sandals clattered on the pavements, a band struck up martial music.

That is how I started on my way home.

XV. *The Drought*

THE peasant headman did not know what to say when he saw that I had come back. He stood and looked at me silently for quite a while. He did not ask where I had been nor why I had returned.

"Go to your room!" he ordered curtly.

His wife, too, looked at me with wide, astonished eyes, as if I were now a different person. She brought the evening meal to my room. It was a pleasure to see her again, for she had always looked after me with great care.

"I am back again, Aunt," I said; but she left the chamber without replying.

I had been away for more than three days. The return journey turned out to be much slower than the way out. The lonely road dragged on endlessly through the unattractive countryside with its few low hills, until at last the chain of our mountains came into sight. Now I was back again in this quiet village which knew no noise. Only a cow mooed somewhere and the tide splashed against the oyster-rocks. When I opened my window around midnight, the bay right to the crest of the beach was alive with the surf of the breakers. The sandy shore was scarcely distinguishable from the silvery waves. The straw roofs asleep in the pale moonlight stood out white against the dark hill. I could not tell which was the dream: the events of the past few days or this village.

The peasants ploughed, sowed their seeds, and put out their plants. At home, the women bleached the twine, wove their cloth, and cultivated silk-worms.

From the distant ravines cuckoos called, larks rose high in the air, buttercups and wild roses were in bloom.

One sunny day followed another and we missed the usual spring rains. The weather was so dry early in the summer that it caused the farmers anxiety. The soil became powdery and the ricefields were getting parched. A bad harvest was feared.

Many of the peasants were convinced that the drought, like everything else, was the fault of the Japanese, because they had torn down so many walls, demolished so many historic buildings, and had ransacked the tombs. This last misdeed was by far the worst, for the Japanese despoiled the graves of the precious porcelain which went with the dead. It was said that all this ware was taken to Tokyo to be sold at a high price. There was not a mountain without its ravaged tombs bared to the sky. Ancient human bones lay scattered under the mountain sun. In the course of road-building, as well, the barbarians had desecrated and broken into many old graves. Often, as one walked along the slope of a mountain, some human bone or skull would come rolling down, causing people to run away in fright. I believed myself that heaven would take its revenge for such crimes.

The drought continued. Many fields were now without a drop of water, and here and there the earth showed deep cracks. The villagers began to carry water night and day. Our only source of water, the brook, dried up, and so the villagers had to walk for hours to bring water in all kinds of vessels from the nearest spring to save at least the young tender plants until the next day. Women offered prayers for rain, kneeling in their courtyards or by their fields in the starlit nights. By candle-light they made offerings of bowls of water placed on simple wooden stands and begged the heavens to spare the innocent peasants from this terrible scourge.

The heavens were merciless. Each morning the sun rose in the east like a fiery ball, only to sear the tortured earth the whole day long.

The peasants had long ceased to sing in the fields. In silence they went out hoeing during the day, while at night everyone desperately searched the skies for the faintest trace of a cloud. Even I never found proper sleep at night and often looked up to the sky. We all grieved, and cared little to speak to each other.

One morning I was woken early by the peasant with whom I lived and saw that the skies had relented after all. Rain poured down upon the whole bay. There was a burst of rejoicing in the village.

Soon after the rains, the weather became hot and close again. The rice meanwhile was saved and growing as it should. Hoeing went on from early morning till late at night. Every day I expected news from my mother. I had written to her and asked her forgiveness for running away without her permission. I was quite willing now to continue living at Songnim until I heard from her again. The headman told me that during the days of my escapade she had not slept one wink and refused to take any food. She had remained alone in her chamber, speaking to no one, so I was afraid that I had made her suffer a great deal. It was with a shock that I learned one evening that she had just arrived in the village. When I came up to her she received me calmly with a smile and merely asked after my health.

Next evening, when we were alone in my room, my mother asked me whether I still desired to study.

"No," I replied.

"Think it over carefully."

"Really not."

"Why have you changed your mind?"

"If I did study, I should have to go to Seoul eventually."

"Don't you want to do that?"

"No."

"Why not?"

"I don't want to go away from you."

"You may go to Seoul," she replied. "Come back to town tomorrow and resume your studies."

"No, I shan't do that."

"Come now. Try it. I want it so."

I did not understand why she said this and why she insisted. I had really intended not to continue my studies. I thought I had learned that the new times were alien to me and that I probably had no bent towards the new sciences. "All right, Mother, I will try," I said at last.

XVI. *Examinations*

M Y school friends were delighted when I returned to my studies. We discussed at length how I could best make up for lost time and get to the university as quickly as possible. If I were to matriculate at our local school, and prepare for the university entrance examination at a secondary school in Seoul after that, I was bound to lose another three or four years. Everyone advised me to shorten this period by study at home and, with the help of correspondence courses, to start working for the examination immediately. This idea appealed to me. I ordered correspondence lessons from a well-known institute for my whole curriculum and began.

At first I got on well. The courses were not difficult to follow and I made tolerable progress in all subjects. After a few months only the English language was causing me trouble. However often I read them, I could not quite understand the complicated transcriptions into Japanese syllable characters nor the explanations concerning grammar. I had no previous knowledge of this language, nor were my school friends able to help, for they had none either. At our local school there had been no English lessons, for teachers in this as well as in many other advanced subjects were scarce. The few native teachers who spoke English were all claimed by the better schools in the capital. I was discouraged, for was not English the most important language to learn if one wished to approach true European civilization?

Yongma helped me over chemistry and physics, Kisop in mathematics, and Kasong, another schoolfellow, assisted me in European history, which I found difficult on account of all the foreign names. My friends came every evening and worked with me until I was tired. All of them had completed our local school, but for various reasons were unable to go to Seoul to continue their studies. This made them all the more determined to see to it that at least one of us should get to the university. Each night my room was turned into a proper classroom, with the difference that here were only one pupil and three or more teachers.

Mansu was the only one who did not help me ever. He had not changed. Seventeen years old already, he still went about visiting his friends without learning anything himself or thinking of a profession. Eventually he became a musician of the old tradition.

He also came to visit me every evening, but not until after the others had gone and I was alone with my books. He would watch me at work for a while and then ask me to come to his room to make music with him. He owned a *kayago,* a kind of string instrument which was always very popular with musicians and singers. Whenever I told him that I had not yet finished my work or was too tired and wanted to go to sleep, he would maintain that so much studying was bad for me. He always had a ready supply of arguments: that too much reading did harm to the human spirit, or that, as the only son of my mother,

I should take care not to over-tax my brain. When all this failed to convince me, he would wistfully appeal to me to go with him on the ground that I was his only friend.

I often went along to his room, which was off a narrow, paved courtyard and had its own entrance, so that you could go in and out as you liked, even at night. This room contained neither books nor writing-desk nor alarm clock, none of the things which every schoolboy owned. In fact the little room was almost bare. In one corner were folded sleeping-rugs, in another stood a brazier with a pot of glue on it. A wardrobe against the wall contained all his possessions, and from this he took a jar of wine and a little fruit in a copper basket.

"Now drink; I have bought this especially for you to-day," Mansu would say.

Then he reached for his *kayago*, laid it in my lap, and opened the bulky old manscript score which was reputed to contain all our classical music. I have no idea how he had been able to acquire this valuable instrument nor where he had found the music. He pointed to a particular place in the score and hummed the tune. I plucked the strings cautiously and slowly until my fingers had gained assurance and were able to play the piece without too many mistakes. Patiently he would continue humming the music and correct my fingering; as soon as he was reasonably satisfied with my playing, he would accompany me on his flute, and we would play until late into the night.

"Oh, Mirok," he once said, "must you really go to Seoul and study there?"

"Yes, that is what I shall do if I pass the examination."

"Wouldn't it be wonderful if you were to live here and

we could always make music like this? You would not have
to work nor trouble about anything; you could live happily, as a human being should live. You could ask your
friends to come and see you whenever you wished, and talk
with them about the heavens and the earth, about the
world and about human hearts. You might have a hut
built in the mountains, and there you could listen to the
splashing brooks and watch the passing clouds. Your
mother would be happy, you would live serenely, and I
could remain with you forever."

"No, I must study."

"You are strange, after all," he said with a sigh.

. . . . .

The year passed quickly and winter came on again—a
very cold winter, but without much snow. It was then that
fate put a tempting opportunity in my way. The medical
faculty of the university issued an announcement about
the forthcoming entrance examinations, which were to
comprise five subjects only: mathematics, chemistry and
physics, as well as the languages, Japanese and Chinese.
English and history, the two subjects which I dreaded
most, were to be left out. This entrance examination for
the medical faculty presented a great temptation to me,
the more so since everyone was agreed that I was better
suited for medicine than for anything else. On the other
hand, the examination of the Medical Institute had always
been known as the most difficult of all on account of the
large number of potential students. Candidates were drawn
from the best pupils at the secondary schools, and even of
these only one in ten was able to pass the exam.

I took several days to consider the question; eventually,

encouraged by my school friends, I yielded and handed in my application. Within a week word came that I had been admitted to the examination and that on a certain day I was to present myself at the municipal hospital with the other candidates from our town. I was instructed to bring brush and ink, a pencil, and a penknife.

It was still half dark and bitterly cold when I walked to the hospital early on the first day of the examinations. A nurse took me into a small room, where I found three other candidates huddled in the corner awaiting what was to come. I knew none of them. All three smiled when they saw me, but their faces were pale and anxious. Then the commissioner came in, called out our names, and compared us with our application pictures. He admonished us to remain calm when being questioned, to think clearly first, and then to write down the answers. Thereupon each one of us received a copy of the examination syllabus which was to govern the next five days.

The first day was given over to a medical examination only. We were led into one of the larger rooms of the hospital, where two doctors took our measures and weight, tested our eyes and vision, examined our spines, our lungs, hearts, stomachs, kidneys, and everything else they could think of. When the other three had been passed, my heart was once again examined more thoroughly, for some reason which I could not discover, and it was only after long consultation between the two doctors that I, too, was at last accepted as medically fit.

We had to arrive for the written examinations very early each morning at a small lecture-room where we wrote for several hours. One day was devoted to mathematics, another to the languages, a third to physics and chemistry. I found the mathematics test exceedingly easy, and there were no great difficulties in physics and chemistry, but the old Japanese and the classical Chinese texts which we had to translate into modern Japanese struck me as so difficult that I was sure few of the candidates would be able to pass in these two subjects. The commissioner sat quietly near the stove with his back turned towards us, perhaps because he did not want to prevent us from helping each other a little. None of us, however, dared to do anything but work quietly by himself. It was only on the third day that a tiny ball of paper came rolling gently across my table. When I gingerly opened it I found it contained the figures of the melting-point of yellow and red phosphorus.

In the oral exam on the last day the commissioner asked me why I had chosen medicine for my study. I replied that I would like to know the cause of life and death. He gave me a smile and played with his pencil for some time.

"That is a high aim," he remarked with approval; "but for the time being what we need is a large number of general practitioners, especially in your country, where general hygiene has been badly neglected."

In the middle of our talk he left the examination room for a moment, and I had the opportunity of reading his comments on the candidates. In several columns remarks had been written below our names. Under mine I could read: Language: simple, clear; Character: honest, gentle, courteous. Under "Purpose of Studies" there was a blank.

Soon the commissioner returned and, after a short silence,

he told me: "You have done a good examination. Your name will be on our short list, but even of those entered on this list, only one in five can hope to be accepted as a pupil at our institute. If the answer you receive should be disappointing, don't let yourself be discouraged. The final selection is almost a lottery."

As I left he gave me another smile and said: "Whenever you speak of 'our country' you should not think of Korea alone, but of the whole Japanese Empire. And whenever you speak of 'our countrymen' you should not forget that you are talking not only of the Koreans, but of all the people of the Japanese Empire."

I did not reply.

Some three weeks later the news came that I had been accepted as a pupil of the medical faculty at Seoul and that I should present myself there early in April. When I came home that evening I found the whole family and all my friends assembled in my room, engaged in animated conversation. Everyone stopped talking as I entered and Yongma came up to hand me the communication from the Institute. All congratulated me. Even my mother, though she said nothing, seemed to be pleased, for she touched my hands several times. After that there was no more talking.

My friends felt that the end towards which they had helped me evening after evening had now been achieved. Soon I would go out into the big world, while they would have to remain in our little home town. Our servants may have thought that I was now lost to our house for good. Kuori anxiously scanned the letter from the Institute, which she was unable to read.

One mild spring evening I went down to the Dragon's Pond Bay in the company of my friends. There, riding at anchor, was the steamer which was to carry me to Seoul. Mansu, Yongma, and Kisop, talking gaily, walked ahead, and I followed with my mother. She gave me her company for part of the way out of the town in order to send me off with advice for the journey and for my life in the big city.

"Don't think too often of the past," she said in the end; "times have changed, as you yourself have often told me. The others are ahead of us in the new civilization. It is true that they are often tactless, but you must remain gentle and put up with their crudeness if you wish to learn something from them."

My friends came with me right down to the shore, which was bathed in bright moonlight. The white steamer stood out magically against the dark rocks. I took leave of everyone and boarded a small boat which was to carry me across the water to the white ship. My friends remained at the pier, waiting until the steamer had turned about and, with a nostalgic moan of its deep siren, set its course out of the narrow bay. To watch the three of them walking home across the hill without me was sad. What might they be talking of? Did Yongma speak? Or Mansu? Were they discussing the journey, or music? Soon, passing between the South Hill and the Fairy Mountain, they would reach the beloved fields round our town.

I was greeted with enthusiasm by the other students on the steamer. Each one congratulated me on my successful examination and all promised to help me at Seoul.

The Dragon's Pond Bay vanished from sight. The tall Suyang mountain sank away. The Suab islands seemed to ride past us so close that you could nearly touch them. Soon we were out in the open sea. All around, from horizon to horizon, the moonlight fell only on an endless succession of waves.

XVII. *Seoul*

Soon after breakfast our steamer entered the harbor of Chemulpo. Here we all had to disembark; I followed the others to the station and boarded a train which took hours before it finally brought the Three Horn Mountain into sight. Hills, valleys, and villages sped past us as we approached the city which for more than five hundred years had been the residence of our kings. Here only a few years ago the nightly beacons converged from all the provinces of the land—those bonfires which, as small children, we had watched from the walls of our town; here the governors had received the royal orders to rule their people. Here had dwelt the most famous poets of our country, and here all the learned men and artists had gathered together. I closed my eyes, lost in thought. The train rushed through a tunnel under the river before it entered a vast station. Outside someone shouted that we had arrived at Seoul.

Picking up my luggage, I allowed the stream of passengers to carry me out of the station. An immense square faced me. In a deafening din of hooting and bell-ringing, rickshas, bicycles, and motor-cycles darted about the tramcars. We took a tram. After what seemed to me an eternity, we reached the main street, with its modern stores, banks, and hotels, and came to the northern quarter of the city, where most of us students intended to live. Here one met students in every lane, in every bookshop, and in every restaurant, all of them wearing uniforms identical except for the signs of their institutes and faculties on cap and collar. Nobody asked what you were reading, which school you came from, or what your home province was. All the students greeted each other and helped each other as if they belonged to a single big family.

Next morning I stood at the gates of the Medical Institute of Seoul, which was situated in the east of the city and consisted of several buildings in the European style. There was a constant coming and going of students in their dark blue uniform with its golden medical badge. Only the newcomers were still in their native costume, the Koreans in white, the Japanese in black. I went with them to the registry to receive my documents, the lecture plan, and the insignia for my uniform and cap.

The chemistry lecture was competent, well arranged, and with plenty of practical demonstrations. In physiology, on the other hand, we did not learn much that was new to us. Anatomy—the most important course of all—was little better. The lean Professor spoke indistinctly, without proper emphasis, and lacked zest. He would take a bone and point to its various outlines and cavities, explaining them as far as one could make out in Japanese, German, and Latin. Since he mumbled and spoke very fast, not even those who sat in the very first row were able to understand what he said. From time to time he would write something on the blackboard, but what he wrote was just as difficult to make out as what he said. One after the other we laid down our pens and sat in boredom until these two hours of torture were over and the lean face had disappeared.

"What a fool!" some of the students grumbled.

The more inquisitive ones among us walked up to the Professor's chair and fetched some bone or other out of the chest, in order to study it and compare it with the pictures in our books.

"Should we not also do that?" my neighbor asked me.

"As you wish," I replied, and fetched a carefully cleaned cranium bone, which I laid before him.

He examined it closely without touching it.

"This is a human bone," he said.

He stared at the bone for a long time before he took it up gently, weighed it in his hand and put it down again.

"Strange," he murmured; "this is part of a human being."

After that we nonetheless inspected the crevices, recesses, and protrusions, and corrected our copybooks in so far as we had written down anything at all.

My neighbor was a quiet and pleasant colleague from northern Korea. He was called Igwon. Medical students usually worked in pairs, since doing so enabled them to supplement each other's notes, to correct each other's notebooks, and to carry out joint experiments. Such a pair of students usually moved together to a pension, and many of them eventually became close friends. Igwon and I lived together in a large, cheerful room. Every evening we studied and argued, one day on physics, the next day on chemistry, then on anatomy, and very often about German grammar, in which we heard lectures four times a week.

For all medical students German was obligatory, as most medical textbooks were written in the German language. Even after we had gone to bed we would often continue to practice our conjugations and declensions.

Each morning we walked to the Institute together, and together we came home again in the evening to continue our joint studies. Together we went shopping, together we took our baths, together we went to the theatre. On Sundays we saw the sights of Seoul: the North Palace, the Park on the slopes of the South Mountain, the Zoological Gardens, or we made excursions on the Han river. Igwon knew his way about everywhere, for this was already his second year in Seoul.

Our Institute was one of the most important seats of learning in Korea. Every famous man who came through the country called there, and whenever some prince or great statesman visited Seoul, we had to march to the station to welcome him. Something of the atmosphere of school—indeed, an almost military tone—still clung to the whole place, as it did to all establishments set up by the Japanese occupation authorities. We were not free to choose the lectures and seminars we wished to attend; no one was allowed to miss a lecture without urgent reason, and even during the hottest days of July we were given no respite from our studies.

No wonder, then, that we were very pleased when the last day of term arrived and we were able to leave and pack away our uniforms for a time. We discussed what we might do during the holidays so that we should be able to continue working together in the autumn. Igwon thought that I was too far behind in optics, so I packed the physics book with my things. He sat at the desk and watched me. He had decided not to go home for the holidays, but to spend them at Seoul, for his parents were no longer alive. He was an orphan since early childhood, and the Christian family that had brought him up ceased to welcome him when he decided not to study at one of the missionary institutes, but to attend the State school instead.

We determined to spend our last evening together strolling through the town, because we had done that so rarely. A twisting lane led us gently along the high, mossy wall of the East Palace. It was this Palace which served as a prison for the surviving members of our Royal Family, and it was said that several hundred persons were still held behind these walls, counting in attendants and maids. Whenever I walked past, I stepped out diffidently and softly. Perhaps, so I hoped, I might hear the voices of the august Royal Family. Vain hope. Not a voice, no fragment of conversation, no footstep reached the outside world. The descendants of our proud ancient dynasty had become quite still.

At the end of the long Palace wall we came to the main street and to the south district of the city. Shops and windows with their Japanese and European luxury goods were brightly lit. Everywhere the sound of Western music was in the air, of violins and pianos, accordions and phonographs. In the garden of the Station Hotel a band played European marches and dance-music. We walked on to the district where all the bookshops were located and bought some novels as presents for my friends at home.

On our way back we walked through the night-fair in a broad side street of the city. There were many stalls and stands which sold old cheap odds and ends, tattered books, common writing-paper with blue and red lines, pictures, fans, pipes, tobacco jars, hats, women's shoes made of silk —all dusty and shabby and to be had for a coin or two. Old men in worn but still dignified silken clothes endeavored to entice passers-by to make a purchase. For all one knew they might have been former governors of some province or district. Deprived of office and function and impoverished, they tried to earn a little in this way to provide the essentials for their families. There was constant coming and going, an atmosphere of bargaining, haggling, and arguing.

On one of the last stands we discovered a large pile of thin bamboo flutes which were offered for two nickel coins apiece. Igwon stopped to examine the flutes. I advised him against a purchase, because they were obviously very roughly made and unlikely to give a pure tone, but he persisted. Whether they were good or bad would not matter much to him, he said, because he had never even handled a musical instrument. All he wished was to try a few simple songs when he felt lonely. So I looked among the many flutes for some which were reasonably clean, tried one or two songs, and told him which to buy. As Igwon made his purchase, a young stranger came up and asked me to find him a usable flute too. I did what he desired. In the end the young man was not the only one who wished me to test a flute for him. An older man and then two women followed his example, and soon Igwon and I were surrounded by quite a crowd of people who wanted to hear me play. I did not care for this. As I tried to push my way out of the throng, the old vendor approached me with quite a different kind of a flute, a true musician's flute made of hard bamboo core and decorated with simple and delicate ornaments. He himself had a similar flute in his hand and asked me curtly, almost in a tone of command, to play with him the Tariong, a favorite classical piece familiar to anyone acquainted with the old school of music. To judge from the flutes and from his way of speaking, the old man must have been a former music teacher or a musician from the Royal Court. Now that European music was being imitated everywhere, he had no job. He was evidently delighted to have found a young man able to hold his old instrument properly and willing to share with him once more the pleasures of a classical piece. Even so I was hesitant, for were we not, after all, at the night-fair in the midst of a vast crowd of people? Igwon had listened all this while to the songs with silent but obvious excitement. Now he whispered to me to do as I was told, the more so since we were not in our uniforms and I would give great joy to the old man. Thus I put the flute slowly to my lips and the old gentleman in

127

his silken clothes began to play. All listened wrapt in silence. No one moved, no one spoke as the musician paced up and down and in a surge of recollection and feeling played before the crowd.

To the south the new Japanese quarter lay before us in a sea of lights; the old Korea in the north was asleep under a blanket of darkness. The night sky spread its black velvet over the Three Horn Mountain and silence isolated the ancient Tsangdok Castle.

XVIII. *The Old and the New Science*

FROM the very first term I was aware that Igwon worked more carefully and more thoroughly than I did. I would be quite content when at the end of the day I had written down my lectures without serious omissions and had gained some notion of what they were about. He, on the other hand, would continue to think about them, discovering new ambiguities and new questions, so that we often had to go through the whole matter again and again in almost endless discussion. Igwon took all the subjects very seriously, but it was obvious that he gave most thought to the problems of physics and chemistry. His attempts to comprehend such difficulty concepts as ether, substance, or energy impressed me. He would sometimes spend a whole evening trying to understand a problem of this nature, with the result that we might not reach our physiological or anatomical lectures until the early hours of the morning.

At this time of night we both began to feel very hungry and eagerly awaited the cry of the pie-boy who passed through our lane each night offering his steaming pies. He knew exactly in which house and on which floor students might be at work past midnight, tormented by hunger. His chant reached us first from the distance, as if a mosquito were approaching. Then the sound became louder and louder, until right under our window it ceased altogether. We heard him put down his case and lift the lid. Igwon, with a smile of anticipation, opened the shutters and took in two slices of rice cake, filled with jam. Then the pie-boy's song would recede again down the lane and we returned to our books.

In addition to his scientific textbooks, Igwon's library contained quite a bit of light reading, European novels in Japanese translation above all, which I knew only by name. One day I discovered several books dealing with philosophy. I took down one of them, called *The Science of Being,* and started to read. That was on a Sunday when Igwon had gone to visit one of his school friends and had left me behind. I was so fascinated by the book that I read the whole afternoon until my friend returned. Seeing me so engrossed, he was pleased at first, but then remarked that I had better not occupy myself too much with the problems of philosophy because they would distract me from my proper studies. In any case, he believed that we Eastern people were too much inclined towards theoretical speculation.

Even so, I found it hard to give up the book because it dealt, so it seemed, with the most profound questions which human beings can ask themselves. It was little use to put the book away and to resolve not to take it up again, because I could not help thinking of what I had already read. Thus, a few days later I ignored Igwon's advice and took the philosophical work from the shelf again.

"The modern sciences in which we lag behind the Europeans," Igwon said one evening, "have not sprung from metaphysical speculation, but have been gained through practical knowledge of nature. That is true of natural science and it is equally true of medicine. Our ancestors always attempted to understand the human body merely from the point of view of the ancient philosophers; it was the Western scientists who boldly opened the body and inspected the inner organs with their own eyes. They ceased to speculate and consider, but tried to see instead where the heart and the intestines were located and how the veins and arteries were distributed throughout the body. It is to their boldness and courage that we owe all modern medical knowledge, which is a hundred times greater than anything that was known in the old times."

Neither Igwon nor I had any acquaintance with old native medicine. Hitherto we had looked upon it, as upon all the old traditions, as antiquated and useless, and had not troubled to learn anything about it. We knew nothing of the studies of the old medical school nor of its views on the sciences. All we had heard was that to become a doctor in the old medical tradition you had to study for at least ten years, so that in fact there never was a medical man of the ancient school whose hair had not turned grey.

Then a lucky incident delivered a rare old manuscript into our hands. Igwon once visited a friend whose uncle had been one of these old-fashioned physicians. The books he had left were to be burned, but one had been saved, and now Igwon brought this precious relic to our room. We looked through the volume, turning the leaves with great care, and found that the text dealt with a section of

anatomical studies. The book was full of black brush
drawings showing the human body from various angles.
Each picture contained a multitude of lines and dots
which covered the surface of the body and these were
inscribed with complicated names. The lines were called
the life-lines, although their course was not identical either
with those of the veins or those of the arteries. At the very
end of the volume there was a supplement of pictures
dealing with internal anatomy, also drawn in black ink.
The shapes of the various organs were indicated roughly
and simply, as if the whole was but a preliminary sketch
of an artist. The outlines of the stomach and the heart
corresponded exactly with those given in our modern text-
book. The liver, on the other hand, contained to our surprise seven small lobes suspended in a row from the left
lung to the heart, which we took to be a symbol of the
small circulatory system.

We smiled at this primitive anatomy, but could not
help admiring the author for his skill in achieving this
degree of accuracy in his drawings of organs which he
had never seen. We knew that no doctor of the old school
had ever performed a dissection. All their knowledge of
what is inside the body was derived exclusively from the
hands, from feeling and examining the surface of the body
with the fingers.

These venerable doctors hardly ever touched the body
of a sick man. They never put their ear to the patient's
chest nor sounded his organs. They only looked at the face
of their patient, listened attentively to what he himself
had to say and felt his pulse. Then they would write down

a prescription which their assistants made up at the time. All the necessary herbs, roots, and plants were kept in the consulting-room, so that pills, juices, and salves were always prepared under the direct supervision of the doctor. Nothing else was done for a sick man; the old medical science knew no surgery, no injections, no ray treatment. Just occasionally, when he thought an illness due to a disruption of the assumed life-line, a doctor might venture to stick a needle into the body and puncture it at certain points along the line.

Why study so long to learn such a simple art? Did the students philosophize and speculate all these years on the meaning of human existence? Or did they spend their time studying the efficacy of medicinal herbs?

Never before had we seen a book on the old medical science describing the anatomy of the human body. They were unobtainable in the book trade, and every doctor looked after his old books as if they were secret documents.

. . . . .

The human body was considered sacred, particularly so after the soul had departed. Then it had to be restored to the earth at a certain spot so that it might return to complete harmony with nature, and would not bring trouble and misfortune to the living or to later generations. For this reason, it was a sin against the law of nature and against the spirit even for a doctor to open a dead body. The early students of our Institute, all of them Koreans, had therefore refused to take part in anatomical dissections. They were quite willing to be taught the modern science of medicine because they were aware that it was far superior to the antiquated native methods; to dissect a corpse, a dead human being, however, they held to be a grave sin.

It had been just the same several decades earlier, at the time when the first attempts were made to introduce Western civilization into our country. But even we who had long rid ourselves of these old notions felt somewhat uncomfortable when one winter's evening we were taken for the first time to the grim building where the anatomical demonstrations took place. With six other colleagues, Igwon and I slowly approached the big table which served as the bier of a young man, an inert body helplessly facing what was to come. Some distance from the table we all stopped and stared at the pale human being which, instead of resting deep in the shadow of the earth, was obliged to lie on this metal board with the winter's sun falling upon his naked torso. Igwon gave me a bleak look and took my hand.

"Not even a little incense!" he muttered with disgust.

The Professor came up and explained that today we were to look at the organs of the abdomen *in situ*. Dissecting a human body was no violation of human dignity, he pointed out. In his view, on the contrary, we were doing a great honor to the dead by sacrificing their mortal remains on the altar of science. He called on one of us to be bold enough to begin cutting the skin from the vault of the ribs downwards. Not one of us moved for some time; at last a student deliberately brought forth his instruments and did as we had been instructed. After that each of us took his turn, and in the end we all worked together until we had neatly laid bare the *omentum majus*.

By the time we had seen all the organs under the flood-light of the operating theatre and were ready to go home, darkness had fallen on the town. At home we refused to eat and could not speak for the rest of the evening. Everything around us: our studies, our philosophy, nature, and human life, everything seemed meaningless and ugly. As soon as we left the Institute I had felt an immense desire to take a hot bath to cleanse myself. Yet at the same time I was afraid of seeing my body and putting my hand on my own flesh. I lay without moving and tried to forget the appalling impressions of the afternoon. Igwon sat at his writing-desk and seemed to finger in a distracted manner one book after another; now and then he uttered words such as "appalling," "barbarian," "awful." At last he found a book which held his attention. He never stopped reading. I fell asleep, woke up again, went back to sleep, and throughout the night, whenever I woke from my fitful slumbers, I saw him sitting over his book.

"Shall we really continue with medicine?" he asked me the next morning.

"I do not know," I said.

XIX. *Departure*

It happened during our sixth term at the medical school. One afternoon as I was leaving a lecture on ophthalmology, I was stopped by a fellow student called Sangkyu, whom I knew quite well. He asked me in a low voice whether I was prepared to come to an important discussion next evening at the restaurant "On the Southern Clouds." I agreed to go, but asked what was to be discussed. Sangkyu took me aside and whispered that local students had given him certain information which needed careful consideration. The Korean people were planning to organize a demonstration against the injustices of Japanese policy, and the students of all the native schools were to take part in it. Sangkyu wanted to ask a few reliable Korean colleagues from our Institute whether we thought the medical faculty would be ready to participate.

Igwon had also been asked by Sangkyu and seemed very preoccupied. He did not speak a word on the way home. We got our evening's work done as quickly as possible and then asked ourselves what the people might demand of the Government. Would it be the right to vote? Or their own army? Or might it be control of local government?

"In any case, it must be something political," Igwon grumbled.

"That's certain."

"Do you realize that we shall be punished if the authorities find out that we have been in on the demonstration?"

"Of course I realize that."

"We will be worse off than the others, because we are studying at an institute which is directly under the Government. Gratitude alone, they will say, should have kept us from taking part in any political demonstration."

There, then, was the big question: should we take part or keep out? We were grateful to the faculty which introduced us to the exalted science of medicine without, we assumed, demanding anything in return. At public expense we had been shown whatever was worth seeing and introduced to the most famous scientists, priests, and statesmen.

Igwon pondered this for a long while. "What do you think we should do?" he asked me.

"I don't know myself."

"If something is to be done which concerns the whole nation to which we belong, we must take part."

"It looks like that."

"What do you think, then?"

I remained silent.

"A wretched situation," he murmured. "In any case we must both do the same."

"Yes, that is obvious."

When we arrived next evening at the restaurant "On the Southern Clouds" we found about ten fellow students assembled there. Sangkyu told us that preparations for the demonstration had already progressed far and that the students of the public institutions had been unaware of them only because we, as "half-Japanese," were not being trusted. Everyone listened attentively and all favored participation. Not a single voice opposed it. None of us knew who had started the idea of the demonstration, how it was organized, or what it would demand of the Japanese Government, but all the students wanted to take part.

Later on we spoke at length of our own ancient civilization and of the cultural achievements of our ancestors and agreed that the Japanese were no better than upstarts. We spoke of the first printing with movable type, of submarines, of the art of pottery, of our paper, and of many other things which our ancestors had invented before anyone else in the world.

After listening all evening, even Igwon, who was the most quiet and thoughtful of us all, joined in with an "All right, then, let us go ahead with it."

We, the medical students, must have been the last to block the movement; now we had joined, it gained momentum and surged toward the goal which seemed so near at hand. Sangkyu often brought us news of more preparations for the demonstration, of flags, of leaflets, of marching orders. Finally he arrived with the important message that the rally was to take place on the first of March at two o'clock in the afternoon and would start from the Pagoda Park.

It turned out to be a fine, warm, and sunny spring day.

When I awoke, Igwon was already fully dressed in his uniform. This day I did not intend to go to any lectures
because I had been given leave of absence on account of
a slight infection.

"Come early to the Park," he said, offering me his hand,
"so that we shan't miss each other there; we'll march
together."

"Yes, of course."

He left the room with a smile on his face.

We had slept very little during the night. Leaden fatigue
kept me on my bed and I found it very hard to rise.

. . . . .

When I arrived at the park at two o'clock the whole
area was already surrounded by policemen and the small
walled-in area was so closely packed that I could hardly
make ten steps forward. Neither Igwon nor any other of
my friends were to be seen anywhere. I stood by a corner
of the wall and watched more and more people crowding
through the entrance. Suddenly there was complete silence
and somebody began reading the proclamation of the
Korean people from the terrace of the pagoda. From where
I stood it was impossible to understand a single word. At
last the speaker finished, and after a second's pause for
reflection a thundering *"Manse"* call broke loose and was
taken up again and again by thousands of voices. The tiny
park was charged with tension and ready to burst. Leaflets
of all sizes and in many colors were thrown up and flut-
tered in the air as the demonstrators streamed out of the
park to start on their march through the city, swept along
by the threatening *Manse* call.

I got hold of one of the sheets and read the proclamation. The Korean people declared that the annexation by Japan had been a mistake and that from today onward it was no longer valid. The Koreans as a people demanded to be given back their right to determine their own fate. I read the proclamation over several times and joined the procession. At the park gate someone pressed a packet of leaflets into my hand and curtly commanded me to distribute them.

The street was densely lined by a vast, astonished, and curious crowd of people who eagerly took the leaflets. "At long last!" some called out, and others shouted, "That is the spirit of our students, our children!" Women in great agitation, some in tears, offered us food and drink.

The police did not interfere in any way with our march through the city. Only official buildings and the consulates were guarded by heavily armed soldiers, ready to prevent any excesses by the students.

It was not until much later that we began to feel hemmed in. Our freedom of movement became smaller and smaller. As soon as we had marched through any one district, soldiers and police closed in on it, so as to restrict the area of the demonstration. Finally, as we left the French Consulate, where we had declared ourselves a free nation without any interference, and made our way to the offices of the occupation authorities, we found ourselves in a cul-de-sac. Our advance was barred. The street was occupied on both sides by four rows of armed policemen, and in the centre there were soldiers. For a moment the two sides faced one another irresolutely. Then the first line of troops burst on the crowd with drawn sabres. Those at the head of the demonstration held fast, but behind them a panic developed and the whole crowd broke. Our cause was lost. After all the glorious *Manse* calls nothing remained but whimpering and whining. In no time the soldiers chased us back into the main street, where another band of soldiers was ready for us and continued the hunt.

I reached home unharmed and went to sleep almost at once. When I woke up again it was dark. Igwon had not yet returned. Restless with anxiety, I went out to search for him. The atmosphere in the city struck me as sinister; the streets were deserted and dimly lit. Everywhere soldiers were posted with machine-guns. Black armored cars raced past me.

I groped cautiously through the back streets to look up fellow students in their rooms; not one of them knew what had happened to Igwon. In vain I went from one boarding-house to the next. At last I met Sangkyu at a corner; he, too, was out to check upon his friends. He had been to see nearly all of them and found out that including Igwon five of our fellow students were missing.

Our room was still empty when I returned after midnight.

The night passed very slowly.

Next morning Sangkyu came with the news that Igwon and the other four had received minor injuries and had been arrested; he asked me to take some food to the prisoners.

Meanwhile the national rising had spread rapidly from the big cities to the smaller towns and thence to the market towns and villages. From my own home I heard that Kisop and Mansu had been taken to prison with other friends of mine. After the students and school-boys, the merchants began to join the movement; then the artisans and peasants, and at last even the Korean officials. The occupation authorities found their position increasingly awkward and asked for more Japanese divisions. Once again troops were continuously on the move, just as they had been ten years before, during the annexation of our country. There was bloodshed everywhere. In a village inhabited mostly by Christians all the inhabitants were locked up in a church and burnt alive. Old prisons and jails were being enlarged, new ones had to be built, and the police were known to carry out tortures day and night. After the fourth public demonstration the students of Seoul went underground and became engaged exclusively in secret service for the movement. I myself took part in the printing of leaflets. After the military suppression of the revolt Tokyo decided to dismiss Hasegawa, the Governor-General, and in his place arrived Admiral Saido, who introduced a policy of conciliation. He disarmed all the officials, who, whether tax collectors or teachers, interpreters or doctors, had hitherto worn uniforms and carried sabres. The secret police, the terror of the people, was dissolved and torture was prohibited. The salaries of Koreans were put on the same level as those of the Japanese, freedom of the Press was proclaimed, Korean schools received equal status with the Japanese, and an imperial university was set up at Seoul.

In strange contrast to this conciliatory policy were the severe punishments inflicted on all the participants in the March demonstration. The courts continued to sentence those whom they described as "disturbers of the public peace" and the police continued feverishly to search out and arrest anyone connected with the movement. Many of those persecuted fled abroad. I personally discarded my student's uniform and took a train home.

. . . . .

Throughout the period of unrest I had rarely been able to send word to my mother about the events in Seoul, and even then only in guarded language. Naturally, she was in great anxiety about me. Now that I was able to tell her all that I had seen and experienced myself she went quite pale; without saying a word she left the room.

I fell into a deep slumber. I had not had a quiet night for months and was quite exhausted.

In the evening my mother came to see me. "You must flee the country," she said.

"Flee?" I repeated without even catching the meaning of the phrase.

I was quite unable to think about anything; all I felt was immense and unconquerable fatigue.

"Yes, you must flee," she said once more. "I have been told that along the upper reaches of the Yalu the frontier control is not as strict as elsewhere. There you should still be able to get away to the north."

I remained silent. I had no courage for the flight because so many escaping students had been arrested or shot on the way.

My mother did not take so serious a view of the danger. She believed that many refugees had succeeded in crossing the frontier at the river and had made good their escape.

This was what I should do. On the other side of the frontier I would be able to get myself a passport and eventually continue my studies in Europe.

Even the word Europe did not give me courage. I knew that it was exceedingly difficult to study at a European university and that the language alone usually proved an almost insuperable obstacle to Asians.

Slowly my mother persuaded me, and I began to realize that I would have to try to leave the country in order to give her peace of mind. It was clear that I would cause her less anxiety by going away than by staying with her in constant danger. I almost regretted that I had ever taken part in the demonstration.

By the following evening I was ready to leave. My mother dissuaded me from staying at our home any longer. Nobody was to know of my departure until I had crossed the frontier.

She handed me a small wicker basket which contained a change of clothes, a silver pocket watch and chain, and a roll of money. This was all I was able to take with me on the long journey to that other world of which I had dreamt so much.

Despite fog and darkness my mother accompanied me a long way on my road out of the town.

"You are not without courage," she said after we had walked together in silence for a time. "You have often been discouraged, but you have always stuck to your ideas. I have great confidence in you. Be brave. You will easily get across the frontier, and I know that in the end you will reach Europe. Don't worry about your mother. I shall patiently wait for your return. The years pass so swiftly. And if we are not to meet again, don't take it too much to heart. You have given a great deal to my life, a very great deal of joy. Now, my child, you must make your way alone."

XX. *The Yalu Flows*

I WAS close to the wide Yalu River along our frontier with China. Progress across the country became very difficult. The rushes through which I had to make my way grew head high and it was only rarely that I could catch a glimpse of the rice-fields or of pasture. Patrols of armed soldiers were about; from early morning till late at night the crack of rifle-shots could be heard in the distance, most often at nightfall, when many fugitives seemed to be on the move. From village to village or even only from house to house I myself was guided by plucky peasants or fishermen until at last I reached an uninhabited hut. Here I was to lie in hiding and to await a ferry-man willing to risk the crossing.

The next night two more students joined me at the hut, equally anxious to be taken across the river. They appeared to be even younger than I. One of them, a pale, nervous boy of less than seventeen, obviously regretted that he had ever risked the escape. He sat on the floor dejectedly and just stared.

At last during the third night an old fisherman appeared and told us to follow him. It was bright moonlight. Afraid of being seen, we hesitated to leave the hut, but the ferry-man convinced us that when the moon was up the frontier guards would be less active. We trusted him, and so he led us by a difficult trail through what seemed a jungle of reeds and rushes. After more than an hour's brisk walk we reached a thicket. Our guide whistled, and soon from the undergrowth came the expected reply. Two more fishermen emerged and led us down to the river-bank. It was a terrifying sight. Here, quite close to its mouth, the Yalu was so wide that it had ceased to look like a river and was almost lost in the endless sea.

The fishermen whispered among themselves and then, as we were waiting without daring to move, they fetched three small dug-out boats from their moorings. Each fisherman took one of us into his boat, and at intervals, one after the other, we moved off from the bank. Paddling softly and noiselessly across the water seemed to take an eternity. When we were in mid-stream we heard shots being fired higher up the river. My ferry-man looked quite unconcerned, but gave me to understand that I must not speak. Later he whispered that these had only been warning shots fired from the railway bridge. Nobody would discover us here in the midst of this shining expanse of water.

We did not reach the other side until long after midnight. The fishermen gave us directions for the three hours' walk to the nearest Chinese frontier town and bade us a brief good-bye. For a time we stood to watch the three boats slowly making their way back to our homeland. Then, without a word, we set out on the rough path, the first time in our lives on Chinese soil.

It was already light when we entered the town. After a long and tiring search we found the Korean inn of which we had been told and went to sleep immediately.

That very afternoon we three separated. The younger one of my two companions left for Shantung and the older for Mukden.

I went for a stroll through the town. The narrow streets were crowded and everything was far more bustling and alive than in Korea. A strange smell of musk pervaded the whole place, and despite all the signboards with their lettering in golden characters the streets looked dingy, for the houses were not whitewashed and all the people were dressed in blue.

I left the town and climbed a hill to have one last look at the river. There it flowed in its sandy bed between the hills, calm and blue in the evening sun. At this point, upstream from where we had crossed, the Yalu was still narrow—hardly half a mile wide. I could almost make out the faces of the people on the other side. They were hanging up their nets to dry. Women and girls sat outside their houses, shelling beans for supper, and children were playing and chasing each other.

I watched the steady flow of the river which separated my homeland from this vast Manchurian country. Here everything was big, sombre, and serious; over on our side all was small and gay. Bright, straw-covered houses dotted the hillside. Evening smoke was already rising from many a chimney. On the horizon the chains of our mountains appeared one behind the other under the clear autumn sky. The mountains were aglow in the sunlight; then, before wrapping themselves gradually in blue mist, they shone out once again in the dusk. I imagined that far to the south I saw the gorges and brooks of the Suyang mountain and the two-storied tower building where every night as a child I had listened to the glorious evening music. It was as if I should be able to hear the heavenly sounds carried to me all the way from home.

Steadily the Yalu flowed. Darkness fell. I descended from my hill and went to the railway station.

POSTSCRIPT

FROM references to historic happenings it can be gathered that the story of *The Yalu Flows* takes place during the first two decades of the present century. Such, however, is the timelessness of this autobiography and of the experience which it re-tells that it is the ever-renewed conflict between the old and the new which holds the reader's imagination rather than the specific events which here bring about a clash.

Mirok Li never returned to Korea. His long journey into the heart of the 'new civilization' brought him to Europe at last, but as an exile from his own country. He made his home in Bavaria, where he lived and worked as a medical practitioner. Here he wrote, almost a quarter of a century later, his book of childhood reminiscences in simple German, a language which he handled with accuracy and immense tact, if not with any great freedom.

In his heart Mirok Li remained a Korean; and the picture which he paints of the joys and sorrows of his childhood has the qualities of an eastern brush-drawing, its warmth as well as its most sensitive delicacy which shrinks from all over-statement.

Mirok Li never saw his mother again. Six months after his arrival in Europe he learnt from one of his sisters in the first letter from home that she had died within a few months of his escape from Korea. He himself died in a small Bavarian town on March 20th, 1950, while engaged on a continuation of his book which was to have described the impact of the reality of European life on one who was so deeply rooted in the ancient civilization of the East. Of the second manuscript, unfortunately only a few fragments survive.

H. A. H.